DREAMS AT THE END OF THE NIGHT

Dreams

at the End of the

Night

Ewald Murrer

TWISTED SPOON PRESS
PRAGUE • 1999

*The publication of this book was made possible through
the generous support of John Bruce Shoemaker*

ISBN 80 901257 9 4

Contents

Dawn will come, possibly, everything is possible — in gazing skyward, a bird will surely sing somewhere in a thicket, or a leaf will stir to announce a creature's awakening. Perhaps I will catch the sound of an animal's patter as it searches in the early hours of morning for its food, examining odorous communications, ferreting about, waiting for something to happen. Perhaps rats lower themselves on cobweb parachutes, or the inquisitive legs of a spider measure off a wall of my home. Perhaps the pigeons are now peering into my window and mentally asking themselves what will I do today, where will I go, what sort of interesting spectacle will I stage for them. Perhaps they mentally look forward to my answering them, to my invigorating them for the ensuing day, to my doing something, something great, that will change their lives, or at least change mine.

townography

For you a feather is death,
and what sort of feather?
Hummingbird's or peacock's?

Simone Schwarz–Bart
The Bridge Beyond

F atigue, excited chatter, a night telegram, fever, a quarrel, agitation, slumbering blood precede journeys — so too these.

A station house, or airport, or hut along the road, or any other connector of old and new, no matter what sort of lusterless mirror, through which one enters into another world, any door whatsoever, no matter with what sound, by what incited sentence.

Some money, handed over in exchange for Mephistophelian advice in a Baedeker. And — the *journey*.

The lights of villages and towns emerge from the darkness; the steamed-over windowpanes reveal the fleeting fragments of actions; the torsos of phrases ring out. Figures appear and disappear. Female eyes with a hint of a story, the waving hands of children, the loud interest of dogs.

There is a *town* — a town on slopes straddling a fjord. There is the quiet of a tavern and the first tasting of the world. I am a stranger here, a stranger who is particular about his mysterious appearance. Silent and enigmatic, I enter words into a notebook — I converse with a white sheet of paper.

In this *town* I caress the snatches of others' conversations. I swallow the phrases, washing them down with ideas. My ears overhear the following:

"I don't live far from here," says a man. A woman looks out a window in the direction of his extended finger.

"Go there, where the sun is, take a right turn, then it's only several paces."

I, too, look in that direction and I see the blood-red disc of the setting sun — a few paces from it a story readies itself. Another man comes to the tavern, stands on the threshold, and trembles. He glances inside at us and looks around, searching.

"You're Christ," he shouts to the table, "you're Abraham Lincoln!" Then he leaves, tottering — an evening drunk.

And in this *town* I am a fowler and the proprietor of a shop full of small cages. I am the owner of numerous colored birds. I attend ladies resembling colored parrots and refined men resembling thrushes. I pour grains into their pouches. From my hand I give birdseed to the young.

I was a guest in another *town*, having accepted the invitation of an old friend at whose side I walked along an evening street. We walked through a gate to the interior of a printing house where they were just bringing forth the next day's newspaper. We gave a friendly greeting and watched the wheels of the decrepit machines as they turned. We took a newspaper in hand, smelling its body and tasting fresh thoughts. We then left the factory for other buildings, strolling through an enfilade of foreign rooms, wandering the heights of the floors and the depths of the cellars. And new rooms grew under our feet; new structures rose from the dark dust of the town. Exhausted, we rested in a doctor's waiting room. We asked for medicine, we requested a sound and refreshing sleep. The doctor handed us sugarplums and lozenges then threw us out on the street.

I fell asleep among stalks of wheat in a *town* in the middle of a field. It was harvest time, and threatened with death, threatened by the reaper, I fled down a sultry road to the town's outskirts. Apple trees lined the way. On each green apple there was a letter — letters of numerous alphabets, letters of numerous scripts. As I ran the trees quietly conversed in the words of unfamiliar languages and incited me to act, to engage in untested activity. In the suburbs I encountered several girls with parasols. They looked at the ground, tears running down their dust-covered, or perhaps unusually made-up, faces. I passed by them without a word and hid in the doorway of a small house. An old woman occupied this house — full of blueberries, buckets and pails brimming with the fruit. The old woman herself stood on a punt and poled along the floor, plowing through the mass of blueberry jam. In the background, behind her head, a flock of seagulls at twilight was painted on the wall. The portraits of presidents hung on hooked nails.

In a *town* with smokestacks and wooden shacks I stood in a graphics studio, running my hand over the lithography stone. I was the journeyman of a golden-curled youth dressed in uniform, girded with a belt. On the stone he painted the massive bodies of machines. It rained — it rained incessantly there. Birds sat on a wooden fence.

In one *town* I stood by the window of an old house, gazing out between the trees onto the street — I searched the vistas to the parks and gardens. Something horrible could be heard approaching, something oppressive and terminal. The sky roared like a pack of were-wolves. I sought the source of the din, which became evident: a dark green cloud was drawing near, or a mist (interesting that in many visions and dreams this apocalyptic mist is often perceived in the color green). During this monstrous bellowing, fiery protuberances were shooting out of the mist in thick columns — flaming columns in the shape of wolf snouts. So along with everyone who lived in the house I nailed shut the windows and plugged up all the openings to keep the malignant green mist from entering and annihilating us. The tranquil, melancholy voice of the young female announcer was still to be heard from the radio as it sadly described to us the kind of terror and suffering the mist was inflicting on the local inhabitants. I fled before this roaring column of mist to the store for food and drink — and mainly for cigarettes — so that we could cope with our captivity in the house. With the other inhabitants of the town I pillaged the shop and then ran back in terror at the shortening of time. And then the mist drifted past the windows while emitting a bellow still more terrible, undeniably and manifestly that of a wild beast. A number of eyes — human eyes — peered at us through the windows. They drifted in mass with the mist, staring at us without blinking, riveted . . .

In another *town* I lay amidst people dreaming in some dark and cosy room where no sunlight penetrated, that was only hazily illumined by candlelight, revealing these figures in an orgy of sleep, — gourmets of dreams, hedonistically tossing and turning in various images. I swallowed some drug, a substance that bore me far away . . . I was a leaf falling softly, slightly lifted back up by the currents of air — a breeze caressed my sere veins and stroked my dry, brown, brittle body. In graceful arches I floated down, back to the cold floor, and the stone awakened me. I lay then amongst these sleepers and envied them the depth of their dreams. I wanted to return to the body of a leaf and take flight. But the dream had run off, it was gone, and having taken refuge in the head of another sleeper, it was impossible to track down. There was nothing left to do but get to my feet and search the faces of the sleepers, to look for a trace of solidarity, to find a timid smile or an encouraging wink. So I groped about their faces, seeking friendship.

And in yet another *town* there was a celebration — perhaps a carneval, or a ball, or a grandiose funeral. I was invited to the celebration. I sat quietly in a corner at the end of a long table and ate something or other, some sort of plant sprouts. I sucked up their juices and was transported by the taste. A petite girl walked through the room. She was searching for the king. Her gait resembled flight for she did not move her legs, she was standing. Her contours were opaque, as if she were standing in another time or in another space, as if she were not entirely here with us. And neither a taste of the vegetables, nor the aromatic smoke of the pipes offered, nor the fabrics the guests laid at her feet, nor the rare breeds of puppies and kittens they presented her as gifts interested her. She asked for the king, and, drawn to him, she flew through the whirl of the ball. The king partially turned toward her and looked at her with a face that resembled death, smiling with fleshless jaws, without muscles. There was humility in the king's smile; he was an unadorned leader. The king smiled, turned back around, drank from a goblet . . .

In a *town* on the seashore I looked for a shop with an antique piece

I wanted to find. And I found it, and in the shop I also found little Liesele with her mother. I greeted them, kissing Liesele. Her mother turned toward me; she had an unfamiliar appearance but it was her. She smiled at me and showed me some porcelain items in the display window, taking delight in their beauty. I, too, was delighted, as was Liesele. Our eyes devoured the delicate surfaces of the mugs and the patterns painted on them by gossamer brushes — and the hands that painted these pieces did not make one mistake, nor shook, nor ever disturbed the austerity of the lines. Then I took the girl aside, away from her mother, for it was urgent that I break the news to her. I finally told her: at last I confessed that I sleep, that I am a sleeper and a dreamer, and all I see, even her, even those beautiful porcelain items in the shop, is only a dream of mine. She didn't want to believe it and laughed. So I turned over onto my other side and waited for another dream . . .

And meanwhile dirigibles were hovering above the *town*, airships — the shadows of machines with red and green eyes — traversing the sky with a predatory gaze fixed on the furrowed fields of the town, with a gaze anxious and wary, the gaze of a mother bird. People were seated in these airships. They sipped their drinks, listened to the radios, and searched the stars with their eyes. The cosmic ships rose to an inconceivable altitude, and the dust whirled up by the great machine of the sky's infinite body grated in the gearwork. The wind caressed birds in their nests, and they fell asleep.

So I slept in the middle of a *town* constructed of eiderdown, bird feather, and quilts. The soft bodies of the plush coverlets pet me and I plunged my head into the pillow. I dreamt:

It was evening, all was a marked blue — the sky, asphalt road, mountains on the horizon, trees. I was traveling by car. At a turn in the road I stopped at a caravan, it also was a dazzling blue. I got out of the car. I looked for the entrance. Blood flowed out of the closed door of the caravan down the steps. A crimson cascade in the blue twilight of dusk. I walked up through this waterfall of blood and opened the door. Blood streamed from the doorway. A sharp yellow light shone inside. On the shelves along the walls stood a number of preserve jars — in them pieces of raw meat. I returned to the car and drove off . . .

My friend was getting married and I was invited to the wedding. After the ceremony the bridegroom and the bride went to the garden. I looked for them there. They were lying in the chapel in a remote corner of the garden. The chapel was full of mud. My friend held his bride in his arms. They slowly disappeared, sinking — they looked at me, their faces not making a single movement.

The landscape of dreams was tense, replete with dramatic turns. I was crouched beneath a window together with a number of other people whom I didn't know. We were looking cautiously outside. Several gray tenement houses stood in front of the window. Tall yellow grass grew between them. Some people were walking in tight battle formation, pounding the grass — from the grass a number of cats ran to our building. It was quiet, neither people nor cats making a single sound. We were overcome with panic and fled to the windows on the opposite side of the building. We lowered ourselves down to the street on ropes. A brilliant sun shone on the other side.

I was with a girlfriend in the cottage of a fisherman on the bank of a rough bay. The side of a mountain sharply towered above the cottage. There were cannons deployed around the bay, and a number of soldiers were in motion. The cannons fired and the bodies of whales leapt out over the surface of the bay. There were so many that the water could be seen for only a few brief moments . . .

And little Liesele Lousshart dismissed me with a wave of her hand and let me sleep. She also entered this town and let herself be held aloft by the voluminous bedding. She dreamt:

Night was falling. I went toward the road, flagging cars. But they were driving so fast only a twinkle of light could be perceived. I turned around and saw behind me the sea — it had not been there before. A partially submerged house stood in the sea. A low wall led from it to the road. I ran along the wall to the house and crawled in through a window. At that moment everything vanished, only the house in the middle of the sea remained. The house was saturated with damp and pervaded by a gray light — possibly a reflection of the sea's surface. In the middle of a room a friend of mine sat with a mutual acquaintance. There was an impermeable barrier around them created by a light, by a peculiar potency that emanated from them. They called me toward them with unintelligible cries. I ran about the house, looking out at the sea and trying to reach it. Completely worn-out, I sat down by a windowledge and observed the sea, over which dawn was breaking. At the moment the sea was becoming light, the radiance around my friend and the man waned. The silhouettes of enormous fish bodies appeared in the water and collided with the sides of the house — and I knew them to be jolts of evil.

In a dream, I saw myself sleeping. I also saw my cat sitting by the bed. It spoke to me curtly and loudly. It reproved me for something — it grew larger, ever larger. As it grew its anger seemed to vanish. I awoke. The cat was actually sitting next to my bed, gazing at me intently.

In a *town* built in the hills, a town of stone towers and wooden annexes, a town of swallow nests, a town pasted together from animal saliva, we then met, and arm in arm we strode through the sun-warmed square. The heat pressed us to the ground and formed red images before our eyes. Herds of beasts ran past in our retinas; these infinite plains of our eyes vibrated with hot wind. A long automobile packed with people emerged out of a backstreet. They looked out glumly from the windows and let the guide lecture on the world around them. As their vehicle circled the square, they hungrily swallowed the houses, tasted the paving stones, licked the cats sleeping in the shadows of the trees, sniffed at the dogs, and lecherously stroked the flowers in the flowerbeds. Everything was thus devoured and nothing remained — the plain Liesele and I had had in our eyes, flowed out from these eyes and was now everywhere. The bus of tourists drove off and left us alone in the wasteland of the one-time town. So there was nothing left for us to do but hop and skip toward the horizon.

Beyond the horizon stood other *towns*, colored and redolent. In the red town there was a Ferris wheel of sorts, wildly whirling and whirling. It whooped and laughed. In the yellow town there were paper dogs; in the green town a lake with wooden ducks; in the blue town a mayor with a head turned backwards — he was looking from a window of town hall at the fields where the peasants were stacking sheaves. Then in the rose town they were flying paper dragons — they were flying on them and they let us fly as well. So we flew on a dragon and stroked its snaky skin. The creature's rocking motion lulled us to sleep, and sleeping we flew over the towns of other colors, liberated and happy. A warm rain came down. We were in a town full of water. Over our heads lay the surface of the sea. The ripples glittered like stars. Fish drifted into the doors and windows of the houses, floated around the towers, under the bridges and over the bridges. It was a town of fish. The silence there was so dense that we accelerated our dragon's flight and glided away from the place.

And below us there lived a *town* full of old men, endlessly riding trams, endlessly standing in long lines at the shops and administrative bureaus. A town of people whose lives resembled the life of insects. A town of scurrying cockroaches, a town of half-tones, half-light, twilight. The objective of people in this town was death. Everyone rushed toward it, falling over each other in their hurry, offering it bribes. The crematorium there was a cathedral, and over its chimney — a spire with a smoky muezzin — stood a rotating column of hot air.

Then there was a *town* of a great fall, of pressured sleep and fear. We were falling through a tunnel filled with smoke having the density of an unbreathable smog. And we landed with a loud thud and were undeniably awakened. Panic and anxiety crept into our faces. We wandered the streets in dread, as if lost. The figures of other people rushed toward us, their stride regular and austere. People marched, and even animals and plants joined them — also houses and automobiles, the water from the rivers, paving stones, and electrical wires and poles — all marched while engaged in relaxed conversation, banal talk, and deeds made material. The march lasted a long time, interminably. The formation plunged into the funnel of a mill. Someone turned the crank and with a smile ground, ground . . .

There were no *towns* and there were no *dreams*. In vacuous space we two, little Liesele and I, took flight — *there was neither light nor darkness.*

the mask

It may happen
that a man over
the course of his life
turns into a demon.

Ueda Akinari
The Fingerless Eccentric:
Tales of Moonlight and Rain

I do not know how to grasp what I witnessed. I do not know what meaning this tale will have for you, — the incident I wish to recount left me with an overwhelming sensation of onerous terror. I understand that I was witness to a ceremony whose symbolism appears to be a reflection of primordial principles, yet I am unable to say what principles, I am unable to analyze this incident. I was afraid to await its end, so I do not know the point of it. The experience was preceded by several other, also probably important, facts. Of course, in my memory even they are shrouded in an opaque mist. I am aware of only the shards that form the allusive mosaic of the story.

I was wandering around a town, more exactly, a large city. It could have been any city. I walked through wide streets and narrow streets, between tall buildings, numerous neon advertisements assailing me on all sides, the cars driving past threatening me the same as the pedestrians walking past. There was nowhere to take cover. In thinking back, what stands out clearest is the sound of the place — an incessant, hardly bearable din.

On a square I ran into two friends, Blumfeld the wizard and Pablo de Sax. They were sitting on the pavement and I failed to notice them at first. I had not expected to find one friendly soul in this city. Both fearfully warned me of a woman who they said was looking for me. But both also cautioned against meeting with her. They were unable to say why; they only repeated again and again that it was dangerous and, as they thought I was vulnerable on the street, they advised me to hide in one of the buildings. So trying to heed their advice, I looked for an unlocked building. It was not easy to find one, as nearly the entire city was locked up — all the buildings seemed vacant inside, and their desolate silence harbingered evil. I finally found one building whose entrance was illumined by a bright white light and whose door was not locked. In amazement I read my own name on the doorsign. I hesitated a moment, but the fear of the unknown woman was stronger than the fear of unexpectedly seeing my own name in an unfamiliar place. So I went in.

The interior of the building resembled the offices of a wealthy, prosperous company. It was furnished with thick purple carpets and heavy curtains of the same color, a number of mirrors, and costly, ostentatious chandeliers. A variety of perfumes hovered in the air; they evidently emanated from the bodies of the attractive secretaries who briskly, and with the obvious importance of their missions, darted up and down the corridors. I infallibly made my way through the maze of corridors to a door painted white with a brass plate bearing my name. Thus I was standing before the door of my own *office*.

I entered and the strange world turned even more strange. The room was not furnished like an office, but more like a luxurious brothel. Still more peculiar, the people in the room were Japanese. A man wearing gold-framed glasses, sitting on a reed mat, greeted me with a bow and smile typical for his people. What's more, I caught a glimpse of a young woman in a traditional kimona with needles in her hair. Then one of the secretaries I had seen in the corridors came in from an adjacent room. She was Caucasian, but on her face she wore the same ceremonious smile as the Asians who were there. For the first time someone who was not a stranger in that city — like Blumfeld, de Sax, and I — spoke to me. She said:

"He's actually quite a likeable fellow!" And it was clear that these words were directed at the Japanese, even though she had delivered them turned toward me. I was then seated by the girl — who was scented with *Rafael No. 1* — on a soft cushion in a corner and left alone.

The Japanese no longer took notice of me. They pushed aside a reed partition behind which appeared a tall, slender stool and a mask hanging on the wall — otherwise the room was bare and coldly white. The woman took a seat on the stool and the man stood beside her. They meditated motionlessly in this way for some time. Then the man took the *mask* off the wall, and I broke out in a cold sweat, for I realized that this was the skin of a human face, the face of an old Japanese woman, skillfully extracted and preserved. The man then fit this face onto the woman. At this moment, without anyone having said a word, it was clear the Japanese were married to one another and this morbid mask was the face of the woman's mother. Then the man ran his fingers over the horrid face, smoothing it out on his wife's. He ran his fingers over the mask more and more rapidly. During this procedure both Japanese were laughing aloud, yet there was no joy in their laughter — they were in a kind of convulsive ecstasy. Then, at the height of this torrent of laughter, the man jumped back from his wife, and while mumbling some unintelligible phrases he fled into the adjacent room where he hastily locked himself in. In the corridor during this brief moment the patter of bare feet could be heard. At exactly the same second the Japanese fellow was locking the door, a female figure in a flowing white gown entered the room. She had no skin on her face, so she had to be the woman's mother. Her horrifying appearance transfixed me to the cushion. The female figure walked up to the young Japanese woman from behind, stretched out her hands, and stroked the woman's hair with fingers resembling shiny black hair needles, the same as those stuck in the young woman's coiffure. All of a sudden the petting changed into a furious scratching. The faceless woman spread wide the skull of the young woman and plunged her head into it, eventually entering her daughter's body. After this occurrence, nothing exceptional happened to the young woman, she looked as beautiful as before. She turned her face toward me and got to her feet. She took several steps in the direction of my cushion. I shrieked in terror and left there in considerable distress, returning headlong into my body, lying in my Prague apartment. Little Liesele, lying beside me, woke up and asked why I was screaming — she said I had been shouting:

"No, no more, enough!"

The following day, as I was looking through the mail that had come, I happened upon a postcard from Blumfeld, a reproduction of the Japanese print Lovers in Bed. *I should also point out that my correspondence with Blumfeld the wizard is sparse — it was the first time I had ever received a postcard from him.*

concierge

What does this mean, we come home,
and you ask us for what reason
have we come?

Kóbó Abe
Intruders

When he woke up he remembered that before falling asleep he had carved some wooden animals. He looked next to the bed, and there they lay — several indistinct four-legged figures. He lay there a minute longer, as there was nowhere to rush off to. When he got up, he gathered together the figures into a box in which were already stored a number of these toys he always carved when he could not fall asleep. This happened often. He held some of them in his hand a while longer, stroking their forms and blowing off the tiny shavings of wood. He shoved the box under the bed. He was now completely awake and he slowly put on his clothes, which were wrinkled and threadbare. An attempt to straighten the creases of his pants, smooth out the folds, and remove the stains occupied him for a moment. But it proved unsuccessful and he let it be. He went to the kitchen. The quiet in the apartment seemed oppressive to him, as he was accustomed to noise and constant chatter. In the calm and quiet of morning he felt uncertain and vulnerable. He opened the refrigerator and rummaged through the wrappings that had been left there from various foods, none of which were to be found any longer.

"The salami that was there as of yesterday was eaten during the night by Patricius Lang!" the voice of an informer said behind him.

He turned and saw the face of Child-Robert.

"He ate it all and didn't share it with anyone!" Child-Robert grumbled further.

"I thought you were all vegetarians," he answered.

Child-Robert gave a faint smile, as if he would like to scoff at his ignorance. He left the kitchen and in the room next-door he could be heard turning on the radio and fiddling with the tuner. He apparently was not satisfied with any station because he eventually left it on one that was playing a kind of music which seemed to be making an attempt at being spiritual. The room resounded with the querulous voices of several people, the protestations of awakened sleepers. Child-Robert did not want to switch off the radio or turn down the volume; he babbled something about its importance for the forthcoming day. The voices slowly calmed down and the apartment filled with drowsy figures.

The wood-carver went to the bathroom. He had an urge to dip his head in cold water and wash the night from his eyes. The bathroom was locked — behind the door someone was singing, the song muffled by the sound of the running water. He knocked on the door:

"Hurry up in there," he said to the someone who was in the bathroom.

"Lovely morning!" this someone rumbled. It was Stationer Seling.

The wood-carver stood by the door a while longer and listened to the water reverberating as it struck the tiles. After he had been waiting what seemed like a long time, he wiped the sleep from his eyes with the back of his hand, took a few steps, and considered where he should go. He heard a din of chatter coming from the room and, wanting to stay clear of it, he vacillated as to whether he should go in. A small group of people stood by the door leading out the apartment to the hallway. Count Herbert Lusperto de Pedurac was helping Carmen von Bülow on with her coat; Paul Linde was shining his shoes; Professor Exner was wistfully observing them. He went up to them and also put on his coat. He wanted to get away from the full apartment.

"Is it unlocked?" he asked.

"Only the concierge can unlock it," Exner replied.

"Who's the concierge?" he asked in confusion, for he no longer knew his way around his own home. He wondered in vain if his apartment had ever been furnished with a concierge. He remembered only that he had always unlocked the door himself. He hunted through his pockets, trying to find the key — he found none.

"The concierge?" said Exner repeating his question.

"Aren't you the concierge today, Count?" he said to Lusperto.

"Not me," replied Lusperto, "I thought it was Carmen."

"No, no, I'm not the concierge," von Bülow protested, "the concierge is surely the professor!"

"I was the concierge yesterday," said Professor Exner impatiently, "I handed the keys over at midnight to the new concierge!"

"Who is it then?" cried out the carver of little animals.

They all shrugged their shoulders. Carmen von Bülow rushed into the room shouting:

"Concierge!"

Seling responded from the bathroom:

"The concierge is Mr. Velebný!"

"Where is he? If he's the concierge why isn't he by the door!" said an irate Lusperto.

"Mr. Velebný!" they all shouted in unison. Only the wood-carver stood silent. He wanted to flee. All these voices were driving him to desperation.

Child-Robert came shambling from his room with a bottle of liquor, his eyes agleam.

"Who's calling for the concierge? Who needs a concierge? Walk through the walls, ye of little faith!"

Exner and Lusperto smiled at him apologetically as if he had caught them at being spineless.

"It will be a long time still before we find the way!" exclaimed Exner, and they both threw themselves against the wall in an attempt to pass through it. But they did not go through. Shrieking in pain they ricocheted off, fell to the ground, and rubbed their bumps.

"My poor little thing!" said Carmen, throwing herself at Lusperto. "My poor little thing, are you hurt from not passing through the wall like you wanted to?!"

Child-Robert shuffled right up to them, holding the bottle of liquor over his fly. He waved the glass penis in front of Carmen's face:

"Drink from the cup of knowledge, lass!"

Carmen gave him a smile and continued to caress the brow of the injured count. The carver of little animals looked at Child-Robert in disgust. This odious person had set his stomach churning, and he so wanted to clench his fists and batter the swollen face of the silly, cheerful child. But the thought of his own skin coming into contact with Robert's skin proved an insurmountable obstacle. So instead of pouncing on him, he turned away. At that moment Professor Exner was raising himself off the ground, saying:

"We need the concierge. We haven't yet reached complete perfection and must still heed all the laws of the universe! The globe is covered by an atmosphere whose confines are a glass sphere, through which only the most qualified may pass. Only through one's own diligence is it possible to learn this vocation. Let us, then, be more diligent, that we may be able to pass freely through the sphere in whose center we currently reside. Once we know how, we shall even walk through walls!"

Child-Robert said:

"Mr. Velebný, who is the concierge, left early this evening. He locked up behind himself because the concierge cannot leave the door that is entrusted to him unlocked!"

These words calmed Exner, Lusperto, and von Bülow. They peacefully faced the wall and waited for Velebný to come and unlock the door. Yet Velebný was not coming. Even so, only the wood-carver showed impatience — the others quietly waited.

"Midnight is still a long way off. The conciergeship runs till midnight," said Lusperto.

When darkness fell, the wood-carver withdrew to his bedroom. He undressed and lay down. Unable to fall asleep, he carved some small animals. Before midnight he heard the clicking of the lock in the now empty hallway; he heard Mr. Velebný unlock the door and enter the apartment. Then he overheard several words, from which he made out that the conciergeship was changing hands. Judging from the voice, the concierge designated for the following day was: Child-Robert. As he was falling asleep in the bed above a floor strewn with little animals, he heard steps descend the stairs, the door creak, footfalls on the street. A dream came to him: the little animals on the floor lined up in neat intervals, and he counted how many days remained until he would be the concierge.

up to the garret
(a celebration of boredom)

And for a second
it suddenly seemed to him
that he was likely sitting
in the right train after all.

Heimito von Doderer
The Waterfalls of Slunj

"Do you think it possible to come to this dinner party with a lily tie in a half-cut?" the otherwise taciturn man asked as we took a seat at his table.

Liesele smiled when she caught a glimpse of the coat-of-arms on the invitation he was holding in his hand.

"To this dinner party you may come with a lily tie in a half-cut," I said.

"I shall select a bordeaux color with a pattern of azure crayfish. The style will then be identical to that of Stationer Seling's ties."

"Are you invited, too?" wondered the man whom we had just joined. "Do you by chance know the lady who is organizing this affair? If you do, then you could certainly advise me in the selection of my complete attire, so as not to offend her taste."

"I know the lady," I answered, "I helped her compile the guest list."

"So, you also put my name on the list?" he wondered.

"Yes, however it is not tactful to say for what reason, particularly in the presence of this lady — she is the hostess."

"Her!" exclaimed the man in embarrassment.

And Liesele said:

"You may come as you are now attired, for as an accessory, a lily tie in a half-cut shall certainly not offend my taste."

CORPUS

The ball is in full swing. Tables of food cover the parquet. All manner of delicacies are here for tasting and for gormandizing. An unbelievable spectrum of colors is displayed on the tables. If you were to raise the silver lids covering the food the most unexpected aromas would astound you. Mountains of fruit from the far corners of the planet tower everywhere the eye is cast. Endless rows of bottles are at the ready and drink surges into sumptuous glasses. And the drink is of the most diverse flavors and lusters: wines, brandies, aromatic liqueurs, fantastic cocktails made of magical juices. And more new viands are being produced. Portly wild boar stuffed with suckling pig, sea monsters — serpents and strange fish — tongues severed from variegated heads, hearts and brains, the spawns and sucklings of the most delicate meat, minute creatures from the realms of water and air, raked out of the hillsides, gained from the wood of trees, the colossal bodies of various animals, blood hot and cold, seaweeds, sweetsmelling herbs, edible flowers, spices, oils, gravies, sauces of exquisite flavors, confections of sublime sweetness — nourishment gratifying the brain, heart, stomach, and soul. Nourishment transporting us to a realm of undreamed of tastes and imaginings.

We are drawn into the rhythm of the dance, into frenzied motions, assailed by images and colors. Ideas materialize and, winding their way between us, cling fast and steal into our embrace, take us by the hand, and infiltrate us quietly. The hall is saturated with smoke. Incense is burning and its vapors mix with the fumes of cigarettes, herbs, and narcotics. Stationer Seling lowers himself on a rubber cable from the crystal chandelier. His body is hanging head down, resembling an elegant spider and shrieking in maniacal delight. Among the tables the ladies play a game with balls and pucks. In the hands of the men brightly colored yo-yos unwind and furl in regular rhythms. Snarling dogs roam the parquet, indulging in their own games. Several guests, stupefied by the delectations, sleep in the recesses of the room. In an open window Patricius Lang, with eyes widened, sings a song of indistinct rhythm. Count Lusperto kisses Carmen von Bülow; their licentious petting shocks no one and becomes an attraction worthy of interest and emulation. Child-Robert strolls through the hall arm and arm with Death, who has gallantly offered to escort him through his world by the grace of a gilded initiation.

All at once we are transparent: we see through one another and no corner of the soul remains enshrouded. All is clear, words are needless. We enter further and further into an unbounded realm of ecstasy. There is neither hunger nor thirst; want is pointless, words useless. We climb the stairs to the garret. Upward to the heights, closer to the sky! The heavens, after all, are our home. This is certain. Carmen von Bülow squeals:

"Up to the garret!"

And the ardent mob recklessly rushes the stairs. We open the door to the garret, hungering for a glimpse of the dust that rises from its centuries-old dwelling, hungering for a glimpse of the play of light between the roof tiles, hungering for the scent of wooden beams. The company spreads out in the garret recesses. The guests slap their thighs, clap in puerile joy, laugh and sing. The tiny body of a bird stirs in the beams; an aroused pigeon flies up in confusion and collides with the roof. Feathers loosened from its wings fall on our heads. The pigeon is stricken with fear and searches for a way out, wanting to get away from our boisterous cheer. The ladies raise their hands holding the balls, which they toss at the bird. The men fling their yo-yos.

"Blood, blood!"

The sounds of throats have merged into one shout of the mob. Panicked and confused, the pigeon tosses along the ceiling, its strength waning, its feathers turning red. It is now lying at our feet in an unexpected death agony. Patricius Lang picks it up and throws it at the ladies who, with dainty faces contorted by terrified laughter, scamper out of the range of the bird's blood. The women's shrieking amplifies the enclosure. The game is taken up, and the small plumed corpse describes parabolas in the air. Then the hands of the guests seize it and cast it on a new flight.

"If you're a bird, fly!"

And again the company runs the stairs, this time from the height of the garret down, back to the hall. We are at the apex of abandon and everything is permitted. We are divine beings, our fate firmly grasped in our hands, each future step within our power.

CONCLUSIO

Disorder in the hall, havoc, the frenzy abating. Liesele strikes the names of the guests from a list for the next fête. She writes on the calendar the words:

"The soiree of morons proceeded as expected."

A train bound for India departs from the station — it is full of gurus. The platform is packed with people, scarves swishing in farewell gestures, tears streaming from the faces. The initiates of *oriental* idiocy grin broadly and puff on little pipes. That is how it should be, it is their way. In a garret lies a battered pigeon.

the initiates

On a calm surface
this topsy-turvy world
can be seen
head down
even despite the motion.

Martin Škarda
Saiph

"You have now reached such a state of anxiety — which spawns tedium — that you may be initiated," was whispered into my ear by the man I had become so accustomed to over the past several evenings, sotted with the alcohol served up in nameless bars, that I could have called him a friend. We were sitting over another of an endless succession of glasses, savoring the amorphousness of the moment.

"You can be initiated into our community. You'll discover that intoxicating drinks are not confined to a waiter's hand, that they are not the prerogative of these hollow locales. You'll learn to know the bottles, to identify the liquids sealed in the glass vessels, vessels you may take in hand and carry with you wherever you go. No more waiters, no more bars. The flasks are already being prepared from which you will serve yourself!"

The friend called the waiter over, then grasped me around my shoulders to lead me off toward knowledge. Given the mild drunkenness anaesthetizing me and leaving me listless, I only vaguely made out the streets through which he took me. Only some corners or buildings were clear to me. Standing out against the gray shapelessness were modern buildings connected high up by a corridor. An unsightly, angular clock on one of the buildings displayed the time, of which I wasn't cognizant. I recognized the towers outlined against the dark sky, and for a moment I realized that night had already fallen. The friend kept on talking, telling me about the sect of adepts he was taking me to.

"Our master is a woman. She is the only one who knows the regulations to which the life of our community is subordinate. We listen to her every word. She is a mother as well as a teacher, a leader as well as a pliant lover."

"That's insane!" I shouted, wrested from the spiritual twilight of my inebriation by concern. "It's simply not possible to place a woman in all basic roles — where is there space left for her antithesis!"

The friend smiled slightly as he answered:

"Insane behavior doesn't exist in the world because there are no insane people."

I vigorously argued with him, for my mind was beginning to clear, the darkness was receding.

"What if, in reality, there were no longer any lunatics? What if they demolished the walls of their asylums and came to us and said they are just like us? What if the end and the beginning of their nightfall lie in the fact that we didn't dare tell them they are just like us, so as not to deny them the singularity of their ecstasy?"

"If I'm insane, then you must concede that you are as well. And if you say you're not, then neither am I. My behavior, or the behavior of my community, is not insane if I'm not insane," he answered.

I continued:

"In that case, I admit that I'm not able to speak about the insanity of negating antitheses, for if I am embodied in you as the negation of your insanity, I believe that I am embodied in you as a man negating your masculinity, and therefore I make a woman of you. And the same goes for the woman who is at the head of your community: a negated woman, therefore a man. Consequently, I could concede that the adjudication of all essential problems by her person in no way jeopardizes the vassals of the community."

We continued conversing in this manner deeper into the dark city, and then I was introduced to the initiates. I was welcomed by a man whose youth I appraised solely by the timbre of his voice. His face was concealed by a mask, thus I had no doubt that I was not to be the victim of a fantasy fabricated by my companion. I was more likely the butt of his joke, but a joke so refined that it would amount to the same thing as a secret initiation. And so I was calmed by the awareness that I would not be cheated out of the promised story. He said:

"We are like the wards of a sanatorium."

It wasn't clear whether he was speaking about the group of initiates or humanity as a whole. The youth continued:

"We are a ladylove who longs to be a poet's personal muse; thus she torments him, and her love for him drives her into the arms of other men. We are a ladylove longing to set eyes on the poet writing her name in anguish on a sheet of paper that has been trimmed for the poem."

The friend and the youth in the mask then guided me further into the house from where I heard the quiet sound of voices. I didn't know where I was, but I can attest to this: the place was magnificent! Though it certainly was not its lack of personality that prompted this feeling, for it more physically resembled a boiler room or a factory basement. In the room where the initiates were sitting I noticed several cult objects: a framed photograph of a small group of men — possibly a different brotherhood or a sport's team — a television covered by a blanket, a wooden tablelamp covered by a green scarf, a convex mirror in a round black frame on narrow legs, widening at the bottom into a stout base. On the central section of the wall, like an altar, hung a picture woven from wool that depicted a mill with a disproportionately large wheel. Under this sacred relic sat a woman, the one I had been told about. Her eyes, heavily lined in blue, were unfocussed and did not bear being given a direct look. Her vulgarly rouge-painted mouth quivered spasmodically with her breathing. The garments of this sumptuous harlot lent her the stateliness of the order's Mistress. On her black hair she had donned a turban, which looked contrived and invalidated her entire appearance.

"Welcome, Brother," she said when the friend had pulled me toward her.

She extended her hand for me to kiss. I did so and she quickly and nervously drew it back. With the same nervous movement she lit a cigarette. Everyone sitting around the table (six other men) did the same.

"Welcome, Brother," the woman repeated. "We are from a litter of she-wolves; we come from a time when snow was the frozen tears of angels and *a killer looked his victims in the eyes*."

I was grateful for these words. I shuddered with a revivified awareness, even though today, I should say, I don't know why it happened like this. When I think about it, the phrase makes no sense. I suppose I better understood the sentence that followed, and perhaps I did so because I had earlier heard it from my friend's lips. The woman spoke:

"The liquid *sealed* in the glass receptacles is *the mother of the poured* liquid, you are the *father*."

This phrase is comprehensible, and I carry it with me to this day, though I'm no longer a brother of that community. It makes sense to me if I grant a direct rematerialization of the body of the mother in the body of the child. So there amongst the initiates I listened to the woman:

"We are from the same litter of she-wolves, from a line of the ravenous, with fine skin that lets us feel the cold."

"What does this mean, Mother?" I asked, for I felt that she wanted nothing more than to offer an explanation.

"*The she-wolf is the mother of dreams*," she said by way of explanation, "the she-wolf insinuates herself into our dreams, driving away evil and placing us on the path to God."

"And this sensitive skin, Mother?"

"Sensitive skin keeps us in a state of awareness, allowing us to *fully believe*."

Sinking to my knees before her, I embraced her calfs in a paroxysm of exuberant, sensual bliss. The woman addressed the gathering:

"Behold, our brother is waning, he has yet to receive revivification, and the bottles in their cooling containers have begun to tip as they head for the void."

So the brothers lifted me up and poured me a drink of clear liquid into a glass, after the downing of which I became fully initiated. I rolled the taste of vodka around on my tongue and dreamed with an opened mind. I drank there with the brothers and the Mistress, and my spirit sank into a dusky tranquility. This intoxication was a boon to knowledge, for I served myself from the bottles, and their shape was imprinted on my hand. This was the beginning of my experience with that wild brotherhood. I visited the community more and more frequently until I became a permanent member of the order

— I was rarely absent from their midst. I initiated new brothers with the phrase that always came to me when I stood on the threshold of the room that for us was a sanctuary:

"Darkness is a dwindled light and bird bones are hollow. We come from the time when all stones were one rock."

And the neophytes allowed themselves to be led at my side to the woman who would give them knowledge.

The community readied itself for its missionary work and we prepared our armor for sacred battle. The night we went out amongst humanity with our message was marked by a waning moon; satellites speedily traversed the sky and the shredded Milky Way shone down on us on the road.

"We are the wards of a sanatorium and we're going to visit a theater that is part of a luxury hotel," said the brother who had uttered the formula of initiation the day of my coming to the brotherhood.

And in the guise of an ebullient party, laden with a number of bottles containing the diety, we started off to the hotel in the rental cars that had been ordered. The hotel theater we came to looked more like a gym. The wood paneling testified to the physical exertion manifested there, the sighs of those exercising emerged from the dark recesses. The interior of the theater engulfed us and left each brother in the solitude of his missionary zeal. A friend and I finally found a tavern of some sort close by. The tavern was gray and dirty, despite also being part of the luxury hotel.

"Brother, this grime is the precious sheen of this locale, for the blackest black graphite begets the sparkling translucence of the diamond," exclaimed my friend, and we drank from glasses that a stranger's hand had filled for us.

"Diamonds are constellations giving solace to the dead, who must remain in the earth," I said.

The conversation continued flowing in the form of glances, through which we entertained ourselves, and smiles, which we sent in the direction of the faces of the others who were there. An affinity to drink, without the cathartic ecstasy, was reflected in the guests sitting in the tavern. At a table hard off my brow sat a boisterous group; it turned toward us and addressed us in abusive language. Our smiles goaded it into clenching its fists, its knuckles turning the color of bone.

"Get up and let your bodies do the talking!" shouted one of them. "Are your fists endowed with the same felicity as your faces?!"

But suddenly and unexpectedly the boisterous group calmed down and no longer took notice of us. Were they pacified by a passive aggressivity or were they laying the ground for an act even more violent and cunning? Most likely the latter, from what I was able to gather from the events that followed.

A girl arose from their midst. She had an ugly face. She came to our table, caressed my cheeks, and sat on my lap. She embraced me and began to kiss me; she kissed my mouth, face, and neck. Her soft fingers fondled my whole body, and her touch forced me to become rigid in ecstatic immobility. The ugly girl, who was wearing an amulet in the likeness of a serpent, took hold of my member and tenderly stroked it. With a pained expression on his face, my friend looked on from the other side. An unreal quiet pervaded the whole room; only the tears flowing from the girl's eyes could be heard, as clearly as a mountain brook. All at once she raised me from the chair and silently dragged me by the hand to the theater, although she did emphatically whisper:

"The serpent does not devour its own tail."

Between the trampolines, which now stood in the theater and lent credence to my impression that this was a physical, not a spiritual, place of culture, a wedding procession was passing. Some children were playing with balls. The girl let go of my hand and ran to a small door in a corner of the hall. I heedlessly ran after her. She was saying something and I tried to understand.

"Physical love is the summit of sadness, only through dreaming can we truly love one another," I overheard her say, maybe to herself alone.

The wedding throng followed our flight with interest. The bride removed her veil, and she was the initiatress, the Mistress of our community. The groom, his face averted and concealed from us, laughed out loud. I was unable to make out his identity by his figure alone — I knew for certain that he was not one of the brothers. At that moment I was unable to distinguish whether I felt from this a sense of betrayal or satisfaction. The wedding guests execrated us. We felt like bowling pins with a ball crashing down. I caught up with the girl at the small door. The instant we stopped, the room compelled me to the habitual utterance of the formula:

"We come from the time when the fruit of a tree was its root."

The girl delivered the phrase. From what I can judge today, perhaps she, too, was an initiate. But I know there were no female members of our community, and I know nothing about the kind of initiation she would have had.

"Trace a *semicircle* with your hand — He expects *imperfection*. He will appear and teach you to know the *circle*."

She herself described a semicircle with her hand, and when I did not venture the same, she kissed me and laughed:

"You will get to know the semicircle of my lap, and He shall appear."

I was confused and, more than at other times, incapable of evaluating my perceptions and analyzing the situation. The wedding guests sang a couplet behind our backs and, while laughing wildly, tossed paper flowers on us.

"A lifeless body is comical," shouted the groom with the averted face, "a paper flower is the semicircle of the animated."

The girl made another semicircle with her hand; her face had lost its ugliness. With calm steps we climbed the stairs that were concealed behind the small door. We came out on a floor and walked along a carpeted hallway. But we became frightened by human voices coming from the distance of the corridors. Their far-off sound drove us back to the stairwell, for we felt it would have been risky to encounter someone. This anticipated happiness, still fragile and unsteady, would have been able in the meantime to unscrupulously jump over into another being as it had yet to live for a while and imprint itself in our minds.

In walking down, the stairwell was different, it had changed. Everything was covered in dust and cobwebs stuck to our faces. The wall having disappeared, we walked down an open-air stairwell, evidently a fire escape. There were piles of scaffolding pipes and floor boarding everywhere — this residue of human creativity, these symbols of uninitiated Freemasonry, unsettled us. I cried out:

"Is the day of my teacher's wedding the day when desire begins, a desire that leads me to a desolate location only to elude me there?

Are you, girl, the herald of disquiet and unfulfillment?!"

The girl was crying; her face was the very essence of beauty, its expression sublime. We went out to the street. I could not penetrate her sorrow and this frightened me. *The serpent around her neck began to devour its own tail.*

A police car drove slowly through the street. The girl lying at my feet aroused their suspicion. They got out and came toward us.

"Look into her eyes!" one of them called out. "Don't forget, we come from the time when eyes were *three*!"

I looked into the girl's eyes and there were three. I clasped here in my arms, she was as light as down. Together we ran to the doors of the hotel. The policemen did not start after us. I distinctly heard in our proximity just their words:

"The scorpion's most prized ornament is the poisonous prong on its tail!"

The hotel doors opened by themselves. The porter rose from his spot with a servile bow, and he opened the door to the elevator. Behind us, the blinds on the windows and doors were lowered. The porter rolled out a hospital bed from the interior of the elevator. Its sheathings were in the shape of a man, woman, and small child. Quiet. The sound of a piano recital from somewhere above was all that could be heard.

I have left from there and I'd like to make public what I witnessed. Where is the source of the vertigo that led me away? Who was the girl I yearned for? What is the connection between the sheathings on the bed and our bodies? Who was playing the piano at that moment? In asking, I hear this response:

"All is only a portrait of tedium, a tedium that gave rise to the anxious desire for this experience."

But I know this answer is a lie. Around my neck I wear an amulet in the form of a *serpent* that has devoured itself. It cannot be seen, it has turned into its antithesis. Only an extremely bright sun is able to reveal, for an instant, the dark spot on my chest.

the nutmaker

They live on sidereal prayers
. . . all see them and yet no one knows them . . .

Gustav Meyrink
Chimera

"It is somewhat of a peculiar invitation," said Lusperto, as he handed me the envelope.

It was faded and had the smell of an old linen closet. The lavender envelope transported me to another time. I removed a stiff little card with the same obsolescent appearance. Liesele curiously peeped over my shoulder.

"Postman Berka personally brought it," Lusperto added, "which is odd, because the last time he delivered the mail in this town was about forty years ago, and as far as I recall, he hasn't been seen on the streets at all of late."

"Perhaps he was waiting somewhere in hiding for just this delivery," said Liesele, and she impatiently held out her hand for the card.

I handed it to her so she could read what was on it. Liesele's face clearly showed signs of astonishment as she announced:

"Factory owner Brůžek has invited us to his house!"

"Yes," confirmed Lusperto, "factory owner Brůžek has requested that our company hasten to his villa."

I took the invitation from Liesele and my eyes flew over it with a sensation of unanticipated good fortune, because for some time I had longed to visit the house of this old and mysterious man. But his doors had remained immutably shut, covered with many years of dust weighted with cobwebs. On the card there was printed in ceremonial roman type:

SKELETON BRŮŽEK AND MORA BRŮŽKOVÁ,*
the owners of the nut roasting plant,
request your presence at their table.

The date and time of the invitation were then set down by hand. The handwriting was shaky, though clearly well-trained in calligraphy. In cheerful expectation the hour of the meeting approached, and we hurried off, laden with bottles of wine, to the nutmaker's home. The doors, like before, were covered with cobwebs. Not even a hint of a living presence was in evidence behind any of the windows. Only in the oblong annex, possibly a storeroom for the nuts, was there a feeble light shining, and the noise that came from there sounded like a group of ballerinas dancing in the silence. The stillness did not deter Lusperto, and he pounded on the gate. Surprisingly it opened quickly, and after a short time, during which we clearly heard the creaking of a staircase and steps, a man dressed in a tweed suit opened the door for us. A friendly smile radiated in his sunken cheeks.

"I am Skeleton Brůžek," he said, introducing himself with a bow and stepping aside so we could enter.

In the dark foyer we had come into he shook our hands and kissed the hand of Liesele. The vestibule was full of stuffed birds protruding from the twilight in odd poses. They seemed to be alive. If one were to look at them for a while, his head would begin to spin from an

---

* Mora refers to Morana: in Slavic mythology the goddess of winter and death. (Tr.)

overwhelming sensation of wings gyrating and swarming. Mr. Brůžek led us along the staircase to the dining room. A banquet was already laid out on the tables. Thus we seated ourselves in comfortable armchairs and ate in silence. After the meal Brůžek filled the glasses with wine and began to tell a story:

"I craved the company of others, from which I have so long abstained. I live in solitude, which, though pleasing, sometimes assails me with intense anxiety."

Liesele interrupted him with the question:

"Where's your wife, why isn't she with us at table?"

Skeleton became quite sad.

"My wife is no longer with me. One winter night she left. Without saying a word she rose from her bed in the darkness, threw a cape over her shift, and in such meager attire went out into the frost. She did not respond to my queries. I followed her but she was lost among the trees of the park, I found not a trace of her to guide me."

Liesele trembled. In a sudden thought I turned and glanced at the window. I would have sworn that I had seen a face in a white kerchief, resembling death. Skeleton noticed my vision and said:

"Yes, that was Mora — sometimes she walks around the house, however she never ventures inside, and all pleas and cajoleries for her to return are futile. I no longer call out to her, and I have reconciled myself to her new essence as a silent, remote presence."

Lusperto filled his mouth with a handful of roasted nuts that had been poured into Chinese bowls adorned with painted birds. This led Liesele to a new question:

"And your roasting plant, Mr. Brůžek, does it still supply this delicacy, so indispensable to gourmet boozers, to the tables of the cafés? I only really know of the little bags with your seal from my mother, who on its account — on account of the peacock that was the seal's emblem — succumbed to the lazy half-light of the cafés and pubs."

"No," answered Skeleton. "My roasting plant no longer exists, they took it from me after Lady Mora left home. They took it from me and left it to become caked with dust. Only some children make use of the shopfloor space. Perhaps they have turned it into a club house or a playground, I don't know, I don't go there so as not to dissuade them. I don't want to frighten them with my aged face and deprive myself of their silent company, which allows me better to bear my own solitude. Yes, the days are gone when Taitl, the owner of grand cafés, would cart off to his establishments whole sacks with the peacock seal; when the ladies would drive up in their carriages, and under their watchful eye their servants would load up my goods, without which the ladies could no longer live. The times are gone when I would be invited into the company of epicureans and adepts of all and sundry secrets."

The conversation then continued over the munching of nuts, accompanied by wine, from both Skeleton's supply and our own. Thus we spent a pleasant evening at the nutmaker's villa. When the sun had long since quit the vault of the sky, we rose, and not to take further advantage of his hospitality, got ready to set off for home. Skeleton, however, stayed us with a ceremonious smile.

"Before you leave me, I shall show you one more room that is for me today the most holy of sanctuaries. No one knows of it, I have never taken anyone there."

We followed him through the intricate interiors of the house. The room he wanted to acquaint us with was filled with an array of glass cases that displayed an unbelievable number of flacons of expensive perfume.

"These are the perfumes of Lady Mora," said Brůžek, caressing the room with his eyes. "I console myself here with the scents that once attended her body."

There were two large windows on opposite ends of the room. One, with a red curtain, looked out onto the park. There, between the shrubs, stood a figure in white with a black cape draped across its shoulders, holding a scythe — Mora. The other window, covered by a black curtain, looked out onto the lit hall of the nutmaker's one-time shopfloor. Some children were there playing a game, without words.

temptation

At present I lie alone on
a ridiculously small bed . . .

Anne Hébert
Kamouraska

The company gathered in the house at the customary hour. In itself, then, this was nothing extraordinary. It could be said that all was as it should be. Herbert Lusperto de Pedurac sat in his armchair, sipping a glass of dark red wine that had been poured by the hand of his wife, Liesele. She had also served wine to the other gentlemen, Mr. Poschleier and Mr. Kever, guests of the house with whom Lusperto had just been conversing. The countryside beyond the windows of the house was growing dark; it was evening and the sky reddened the room. At the moment the walls were turning crimson someone pounded on the gate with a resolute, perhaps even a nervous, knocking.

"A visitor at this hour must be bringing important news," said Lusperto, "I cannot imagine an ordinary and insignificant caller at our door at this time of day."

They waited to see who would enter, hearing the opening door, the brief conversation with the doorman, the stairs being ascended, the steps in the halls. The door to the salon opened and the visitor entered —a swarthy visitor, unknown to the gentlemen. Yet Liesele had visibly become distraught, the visitor had unsettled her. Lusperto rose and, with a quizzical countenance, strode up to the visitor.

"I am Ion Lupulescu, I have just flown in from Bucharest," said the visitor, introducing himself.

"And what are you looking for in this house?" asked Lusperto, astonished.

"I am looking for a girl in this house," answered Lupulescu.

Lusperto no longer said a thing. He motioned to Liesele; she was the only woman in the house and besides, she had just flown in from Bucharest not more than an hour ago. Here, then, was the connection. Clearly the visit was for her. Lupulescu hastily walked up to Liesele and solemnly kissed her, it could be said with excessive solemnity, even confidentially, and with a considerable dose of indecent allegory. Liesele seated him at the table and poured him a glass of dark red wine. In a moment all were sitting at the table and drinking the dark red wine. Lusperto attempted to resume the interrupted conversation with Poschleier and Kever, but their chatter was contrived; it was not possible to take up again the topic. Liesele talked with the Rumanian, and their conversation confirmed the suspicions of those present: they had flown in together, and had become acquainted, on the last flight from Bucharest.

Their preoccupation with one another seemed vulgar and indecorous to Lusperto and his friends — mentally they especially reproached Liesele. After a short while Lusperto could no longer bear it and quit the company, leaving the room. He paced the terrace, smoking a cigarette. Poschleier and Kever did the same. So together they smoked cigarettes and from the room the voices of Liesele and Lupulescu struck their ears.

"This situation should be resolved," said Poschleier.

"How?" asked Lusperto.

"Let's throw the Rumanian out of the house!" proposed Kever.

Lusperto nodded and they then went back into the room. They

seized the Rumanian Lupulescu and led him out to the front of the house without any difficulty, as he did not resist. He walked off without even looking back.

"A bit peculiar," Poschleier said of the incident.

Standing on the terrace, Liesele watched the man depart.

"A sign, if it were to be genuine, a sign from the heavens to convey the import of the event!" called out Lusperto who was standing behind her.

"Look!" suddenly shouted Kever.

A plane, a wooden vessel of enormous proportions, a winged ship, was drifting dangerously low over the hills. The body of this machine was so immense that in passing it darkened the sky. It drew nearer the house, and the ingenious ornamentation carved into its side could be observed from the terrace. It was a magnificent sight — the sky completely hidden by a wooden machine that was reflected, together with the peaks of the mountains, on the surface of the lake below.

"The plane from Bucharest," said Lusperto.

"Look, Liesele, the plane from Bucharest is approaching, just like the one you came in on today. Isn't the fact that it's flying over our house a sign? Let's wait for some detail that will enable us to decipher the precise meaning of this communication!"

The wait was not long for the plane suddenly ended its fly-over with a booming clatter upon striking a rock ledge. Some figures went scurrying along the deck: an old man in uniform and several young women. Clutching the frames of opera glasses and binoculars, the company on the terrace could only mutely watch the catastrophe. The vessel tumbled over and rolled down the mountain slope toward the lake, where it stopped for a moment on the surface of the limpid water.

It straightened up, and quietly, with dignity, sank to the bottom. The clear water made it possible to follow the entire descent. The craft sank slowly and disappeared in the depths, jolting and quaking against the stones on the bottom.

The captain, the old man in uniform whom the company had spotted in the air, swam ashore. The women could be seen, now on the bottom, sitting dead in armchairs, swirling around in them, swirling — winding their way upward, toward the surface.

"This was the sign we've been waiting for!" said Lusperto, and the whole company left the terrace.

Lusperto closed the casement and went to bed.

In the morning Lusperto went for a walk to the lake. He found the prints of five pairs of girl's feet in the sand of the bank. The sole-prints of the dead women's souls. When he returned home, he said to Liesele:

"Your child is crying, go comfort little Rosali."

And Liesele went and comforted little Rosali.

an experiment

A tear rolls back into its eye.

Paul Celan
Breathturn

"**H**as every effort been in vain?!" exclaimed Paul Linde, feeling that after years of work he would never reach his objective.

The long years of research seemed to have been squandered: He never captured the gaze of his media, he never succeeded in enclosing it in an isolated space and precipitating its essence. He was tired, and a bitter disappointment, taking the form of cogitations on the futility of intentions, had stolen into his thoughts.

"Am I a lunatic, are my ideas diseased nonsense?!" he cried out, his voice ringing with impotent sorrow.

At that moment, when he wanted to consecrate his defeat, someone rapped on the window. Paul Linde's workshop was in an isolated location amid the city's outskirts, somewhere on the edge of the Prague district of Malešice in a labyrinth of wooden fences and small open spaces strewn with rubbish. Linde, unprepared for a visit, jumped up from his chair startled, fixed his eyes on the window, and tried to make out the face behind it. The man standing behind the window, a well-groomed fop in an ostentatious suit, inspired trust, so Linde unlocked the door and let the visitor in.

"What do you want?" he inquired with resigned ingenuity.

"I would like to complete your experiment," said the unkown man, "I know that it's possible."

"Who are you?" asked Linde.

"I am Professor Exner," the unknown man introduced himself. "You can find my name mentioned in both the specialist literature and the popular press. You would know my face from the photographs in the newspapers and from television if you weren't such an antiquarian cloistered amid your research."

Paul Linde, to whom the words "press" and "television" meant nothing, did not respond. So the man continued:

"Since I am a renowned scientist I really shouldn't have to explain how I came to learn of your project," he hesitated for an instant before adding, "Colleague Linde."

He scrutinized the recluse's eyes to see whether he had noticed the meaningful pause and fully sensed the aloofness which Exner thought important to emphasize. Paul Linde, however, did not display any feelings — he had none. Thus the learned Exner continued with his soliloquy:

"I have followed your experiments from a distance and have been engrossed in speculations as to when you would finally determine that you are not capable of bringing them to conclusion. Naturally I know how to obtain the essence of a person's gaze. Some time ago I successfully made use of several media in this manner. For the meantime, I have not presented my discovery to the general scientific community because, purely from caprice, I would like to grant you the pleasure of undersigning this discovery. This is the reason why I'm here, to show *you* the process.

"So then, *in medias res*: Not least important for a successful work is the attire of the investigator. Take a look at my elegant appearance: my banana blazer ingeniously covered by a safari jacket in a shortened length — the latest in world fashion — worked into a tight-fitting cut.

Look here, the jacket is adorned with sewn-on pockets and a belt. The material is a polyester-cotton blend in a never-before worn beige color; as a complement to this I have stylish synthetic wool pants closely fitted and widening at the bottom to twenty-eight centimeters, with a belt and oblique walnut-colored pockets.

"Of course even more important than one's clothes is the entire world-view of the scholar and his relationship to humankind. My heart is gladdened by the devotion of the matter that kneels down before me and reveals to me all its mysteries and secrets. Thus my faith in humanity, for whose prosperity and general felicity I undertake my scientific work, is unshakeable. I would like humanity to give me its knowledge and in return I give it mine. I am its brother, a welcomed guest at debating societies as well as at family gatherings. I speak with people in the manner of their natural, simple soul, and they love me. And it is just that they love me, for I am their servant, a servant who gives them all the fruits of his spirit selflessly and with genuine love. Not sealing myself off in a false solitude, I work right in the midst of these dear people. Whatever I would create apart from them would have no use value for them. And I emphasize, the justification for my research is really all as a service and good work intended for their use."

Goggle-eyed, Paul Linde followed Exner's unreal figure moving about the interior of his workshop so inorganically. He could not understand how Exner had still not smashed all the ancient glass-ware that enveloped him and that had become ridiculous, useless pieces of junk in his presence. He could not understand why the paint had not yet peeled from the venerable portraits that decorated the walls of his study — all these faces, compared to Exner's face, with its tender quintessence of all that is good from industrious and upstanding common folk, paled in their impassiveness and insignificance. The magnificent Exner spoke:

"So then, we shall begin at once. I am here, dear fellow scientist, to guide you."

His voice was warm, sanguine by its openness.

"Concentrate your thoughts, there is an operation I would like to perform. Become my medium yourself!"

With a friendly smile Exner walked up to Linde and quickly put him into a deep hypnotic sleep. With several weary movements he then removed the eyeballs from Linde's head, deposited them into an alcohol infusion, screwed on the cap, and placed it inside his briefcase. Linde, now deprived of eyes and submerged in darkness, sat on his chair incapable of doing anything. He no longer took notice.

As he was driving past the château of Baron Elbers in Hrdlořezy, Exner glanced for a moment at the flowering *Liliodendron Tulipifera* in the garden and smiled in satisfaction. "I'm perfect," he thought, "I'm not one of those amateur thieves somewhere abroad, — somewhere in sunny Italy — who break an egg on the head of their victim so that under the pretext of lending a hand with cleaning off the mess they may run off with the victim's coat through the labyrinth of narrow lanes. For them a coat is valuable booty, though what a far cry from the preciousness of my booty!"

end of the circle

. . . any kind of implied theory,
could even be the truth . . .

Paul Linde
The Grim Reaper in Aachen

A set of complex measurements and calculations was about to take place. A concentration of figures was bent over a diagram. An old man quickly waved his hand holding a wooden compass that was enormous compared to the size of the drawing. The young, athletically built men followed the circling hand, the professor's gestures. Concentrating, they wrote down his words into their notebooks. Then, as was expected, the door opened and an inconspicuous young man entered the study. The bowed heads greeted him deferentially. The old professor turned toward him, as all present had mentally assumed, and bowed to the inconspicuous young man, whose face was not overly attractive, whose body was not overly athletic, it was even a little corpulent.

"Through these steep calculations we are looking for the end of the circle," said the professor and the students emphasized: "the end of the circle."

Roller — he was the young man — took hold of the large compass and jabbed it into the middle of the circle. The professor and the students listened to his hush-voiced computations:

"The first measurement — the number of homes on the streets through which you have passed.

The number of windows in them.

Discarding the incorrect numbers.
Arriving at the mean.
A window with white curtains, recently washed, fragrant.
A figure in this fragrant apartment.
Descending the stairs.
The sound of keys in a pocket.

The second measurement — the purpose of the journey,
a progression of thoughts sliding away.

The third measurement — the journey, expectation."

Roller straightened up and said to the professor and students:

"We must now clarify the essence of the circle. There are recurrent events on this journey — in the life of an individual a succession of details circle the center, circle the essence or possibly the soul, the original thought or intention. Thus we now have the disqualified essence of our academic (sample) circle: the figure from the apartment with the white curtains, whose idea is a journey. We also know that this journey is repeated, it is a circle. It comprises tiny numbers, points, thoughts, imaginings, aspirations."

Continuing on, Roller presented this episode to the mind's eye of those present:

"Consequently this figure, a girl, went down the stairs. She exited the building out to the street on which high, today now old, houses are constructed. She took the keys from her pocket, unlocked the garage door, unlocked the car, and drove off. She drove down a wide road lined with towns. The numbers ran quickly in the opposite direction, thus she was approaching negation. After some time she arrived in the town she had wanted to reach. She came to a stop by a curb on a street with different old houses. She locked the car, opened the door, and walked up the stairs. She unlocked the apartment, went in, quickly passed through the entranceway to a room, and opened a window covered by white, freshly washed curtains. From the window she looked out at the car parked by the curb. She then sat in an armchair with a book she had just taken from the bookshelf, opened it to pages at random, and read. The room became torpid through the torpor of the reading girl.

"And in another town, as we are assuming, at precisely the very same moment, in an armchair behind white curtains sat another girl reading a book, the pages of which, however, were not opened at random. She was the friend of our sample figure. She was reading a book, and from time to time she glanced up at the clock, for she was waiting for the moment it would be time to leave the house. The girls had arranged a meeting. They were meeting, then, at the same point of the circle: the expected time of their meeting. They met in a café. Upon greeting one another they each extended both hands and thereby created the form that we are investigating. Over coffee they each notified the other of what had happened in their lives since they last parted.

"They met regularly in this manner, either in the town of the first girl or in the town of the second. Invariably they marveled at the similarity of their private experiences. In this way they felt like sisters even though they were from different bloodlines. The startling similarities elated them. They laughed and their mouths formed circles. Their earrings, rings, and bracelets also must be included in our computation.

And perhaps somewhere here, Professor, we are at the essence of the theory of the circle. But if we were to compute all the variables, how distant we would still be from its end! We still have a long way to go toward completing the calculation."

The students stood above the drawing in deep thought, as did their professor. At that moment Roller left the room. The professor bent over the sheet of paper, having taken the compass from it. He remarked quietly:

"Gentlemen, we have arduous work ahead of us."

juliana

Each of us has only
one garden,
don't look for me in others.

Jana Máchalová
Stay Mine

"Give me your hand, Juliana, for sincerity and pure words are not to be found anywhere in the world. So give me your hand, Juliana, and together we'll leave this house which has been our world, where we have grown used to living. We'll go out to the garden, where there is prodigious space and a towering sky. Don't be afraid, Juliana, firmly take my hand and let yourself be led. Don't you remember, have you forgotten, those evenings we would light a fire under a black sky and let ourselves be carried off by words which were incomplete, bounded by the low ceiling? Even our souls will surely feel better in the open space and our lives will be infinite, for each thought that issues from our minds will wander the vastness of the cosmos and never return. In this way it will stay pure, existing in the form of a precise crystal, never to be repeated, never to be multiplied by its reverberation, by its eternal journey, from wall to wall, from ear to mouth. So give me your hand, Juliana, come down to the garden, for evening is drawing near and the wisdom of dusk is emerging from the gorse. Today, and from this day on forever, let's leave our ears deaf to the beckon of the bell that summons us to dinner, that binds us to the austere ethos of this house." And Lusperto walked out with Juliana. Their footsteps violated the newly raked sand of the garden paths and they proceeded together to the most remote regions of the garden: to where it grows over into a park and ultimately into open nature, to where human influence vanishes in the sempiternal order of nature, to where diminutive human souls are imbued with the self-evident, formidable intent of the demiurge's spirit.

Lusperto and Juliana left the house and sat down in the sweet smelling grass, the fragrance of which brought them to a state of bliss and let them forget, and possibly overcome, the subconscious fear of the bell's ring, with which the servants summoned them to meals — allowing them to understand this bell as only a sound, as a mere clang of metal, without meaning.

And Lusperto said to Juliana:

"Your dress is white and ironed smooth, your perfume is perceptively chosen, symbolic for the coming moment. You are scented like a breeze that, having broken free from a gale current, wanders through the world alone in its predestined ephemeral existence. You are scented like a star that, having abandoned its millennia-long post, breaks free to fall through space and experience the giddiness of falling, the giddiness of a rapid pilgrimage that surely has no purpose, finding instead completion in the transient plunge. You are scented like a young beast who without the caution of an experienced predator has set off to an unfathomed span of forest, intoxicated by the unknown, unaffected space. You are scented sensuously as an unripe girl, giving herself out of ignorance to her aged lover's embrace."

And Juliana said to Lusperto:

"My head is spinning and I'm afraid, afraid and deeply distressed, dazzled by the boundlessness of the sky over our heads."

And it was evening and the beginning of the night of the first day in which they had abandoned their home.

In the house an old count was coming to a set table. Startled by the absence of Juliana and Lusperto he impatiently clinked his spoon and gripped the hand of the old countess, herself unsettled. Celestin, a guest of the house, a quiet natural scientist of low birth stringently adhering to the rules of family guests, became disconcerted. On the countess's command, when another considerable moment had passed, the servants began to bustle and swarm. They set about searching the chambers, and with their lamps they examined each room, which until then had been submerged in a gloom of purposelessness and dereliction. After a while the servants went out to the garden where their compliant legs took off running the breadth of the park. The scintillating lights illuminated the corpus of the shrubbery and lit up the sleeping flower beds. And Lusperto, with Juliana asleep in his arms, was discovered in a corner of the garden. The discovery was celebrated and tartan rugs were brought out, as were warm drinks for slaking the chill that may have been gnawing the insides of the young woman.

The aged countess then interpreted the entire episode as was natural for her, as she had made sense of similar occurrences in the house — she covertly celebrated the engagement of Juliana to Lusperto. And she was willing to forgive the unforgiveable, for the situation lent itself to explanation and forgiveness. Therefore Lusperto rose from the flattened patch of grass and said:

"Esteemed lady, mother of my dear Juliana, — my dear creature who for the first time has liberated herself and thrown off the fetters of the house — it is not my intention to take your daughter for a wife and carry her off to my home. I would rather Juliana be called a friend, a fellow-traveler among the stars, for our eyes have already set out on a pilgrimage, and they wander the far regions of the cosmos; it was my intention to bring her to the garden, for the garden is the one place where a body, enveloped by the Creator's world of untrammeled nature and the fruits of the human spirit, attains calm. Thus I kneel before you and pay homage to your cultivation — I beseech you to give me Juliana, give her to me for a journey through the garden, for a journey that will last an eternity."

The countess regarded Juliana and Lusperto and quietly answered in a voice ringing with terror:

"Your supper is on the table and getting cold. Your wine is going flat in the glass, its savor wandering lost under the dining room's vaulting. Your serviettes are untouched and their whiteness, untarnished by your fingers, screams."

And Juliana said:

"Mother, since my fingers touch the stars, there is no need for them to touch the slaughtered beasts we were in the habit of eating, as such beasts are only a small portion of primordial matter. And there is also no need to listen to the ringing of the bells that demarcated our time, as this ringing is only a paltry fragment of primordial time, which is inert."

The countess saw that Juliana's eyes had lost expression and that her mind had become absent. And the countess saw Juliana's body shake with convulsions and a lunatic grin come to her face. She then became deeply afraid. For a long time she tried to persuade her to return home, as did the old count, but it was to no avail as neither Juliana nor Lusperto heard their voices. In the silvery voice of the stars they repeated over and over:

"We are faraway, happy, our souls walk in the bluish realms of the cosmos; there is no longer pain and sorrow."

The weary countess gave a nod to the servants to seize the bodies of the young nobles and drag them off to the house where they were to be strapped to beds and have the sickness driven from them by the usual methods. The servants went to seize Lusperto and Juliana, but they could not grab hold of them. Their arms swept through the air and clashed into one another in an odd sort of applause, as if they had been trying to catch a nebula. Panic was reflected in the faces of those present.

carmen von bülow
(a romance tale)

With ardent deceit I love you . . .

František Halas
The Cock Startles Death

"You're asking that I divulge to you the source of my sorrow. But if I were to tell you, which I have considered, you would not believe me, and would no doubt take me for a dreamer clinging to the decor of an age long gone, a romantic who doesn't want to come to terms with the age in which he lives, an age he rejects as it does not conform to his ideas. We have been brought together by a journey, by the prosaic circumstance of sharing a train compartment. Writers have portrayed and utilized this particular situation many times in the past, and in such disgraceful superficiality you have asked me to elucidate the reasons for my sadness."

It seemed that the man was irritated by my request, and he did not take up the conversation. His sadness was so palpable I could not restrain my desire to ask more questions. I was eager to learn what had created a sorrow so monstrously solemn and such a perfect monolith — an august monument to grief. However, the man again began to speak:

"I could change locations and request a separate compartment, make a bow and depart, thereby leaving you here alone with the shadow of my sorrow. But you wouldn't be able to bear such a large and empty vessel. So I shall fill this vessel with the story of my misfortune, so that it will stay balanced in your hands and not shatter into another tragedy."

My curiosity was piqued; it actually did resemble a vessel craving something to fill it. I was eager to hear his story, even though it was likely to trouble me. I longed for the weighty relief knowing would bring. The man fixed his eyes on me and continued:

"I shall tell you, then, my story. I am Count Herbert Lusperto de Pedurac. My name may surprise you as at this time it is somewhat uncommon in Bohemia, but be sure that this is my true name. I was born in Prague, somewhere en route between my father's writing desk and my mother's easel. I then had the carefree childhood of a demiurge. Later I became a gardener. I wed a model, begot a daughter, separated from my wife, then spent several years at the side of coquettes — but none of this is important. This is merely a trivial story of a life in shadow. The source of my sorrow lies elsewhere. This past life only compelled me to recklessness. The story that follows is likely to leave you cold and perhaps conjure up an astonished smile on your face. But be aware that it is this very tale which I am about to tell you that is the prime cause of my sadness. The whole of it was really a kind of consecration ritual."

The man fell silent. He searched my face, as if in my eyes he were looking for an answer to an unstated question. To avoid his eyes, which were indeed sad, I preferred to gaze out the train's window onto the countryside running past. The train passed strip-mines, a landscape strewn with the chimneys of power plants. Amid these gray planes I caught a glimpse of a small chapel with a cross, and was amazed that it was still standing. I noticed there a flickering white figure, — perhaps a ghost or Death. Yet when my view to the landscape took a half-turn, and another aspect was placed before my eyes, I understood that the white figure was merely a shirt flapping on the building like a flag, and that the building was not a small chapel but a workers' barracks mounted by a television antenna. Lusperto, too, looked out the window and sighed as he said:

"Perhaps a ghost, perhaps Death."

This made me shudder. His clairvoyance compelled me to ask:

"Please, tell me your story."

This is Lusperto's tale:

"I was working at that time in the gardens at Prague Castle, in the gardens where, at the break of dawn, one may catch sight of the shades of noblewomen leaving their institute — today occupied by the police — the shade of Rudolf II or Charles IV, the dark figure of Heydrich or the absent-minded shades of Dubček and Svoboda, planting linden trees, or even Masaryk carving sentences into his stone table. In mentioning the Institute of Noblewomen, I have touched upon my sad initiation. A woman worked there whose name, the name she used in introducing herself to me, attracted me to her and drove me to becoming her shadow. Carmen von Bülow: the bearer of a name weighted by the tradition of a family she had nothing to do with. She had chestnut brown hair and a face illuminated by melancholy. How captivated I was by this face, without ever suspecting that its dreamy melancholy was the beginning of frightful sorrows. She came from a small town in eastern Bohemia. The place is not important; nothing about the place is important for my story. Yet the name of her birthplace became a magic spell for me. I would look for this name on every map, even astrological maps, and I would cut it out of these maps and carry it in my pocket. I was madly in love with her, and she returned this with devotion. She was the embodiment of innocence; she was beautiful and pure. Again, all of this may seem rather banal to you, merely a story that has been experienced numerous times. In recounting it, I shall attach the shards of the relationship that have remained. Maybe they will help you to perceive the terrible allegories lurking in amorous gestures, for that is where the monstrous seed which blossoms into sorrow is sown. Listen carefully to what I have to say; everything I shall tell you is important."

He was interrupted from continuing with his tale by the conductress who had come to check our tickets. She smiled at us: at me with the requisite politeness, but at Lusperto with sad understanding.

"Have you ever noticed the women you pass by?" Lusperto asked when she had left. "Their eyes reveal that they know everything, that they know the cost of sorrow. How horrible it is that through the instruments of fate one is able to glimpse into purpose; how painful such knowledge must be!"

He was silent for a moment and sighed. He now acted deplorably; his dignity vanished.

"Have you noticed that train conductresses have concubine eyes?" he then asked.

I scrutinized his face. It seemed ordinary: a short, trimmed beard; moderately thinning hair smoothed back; wide lips and an unhealthly complexion; a rather round face. A lake appeared on the other side of the window. From its surface rose the arches of a washed-out bridge. An icy setting.

After a while Lusperto again addressed me: "Listen, then, to these little tales that for me became fateful."

"Carmen and I were sitting in a winebar, and of course it was bathed in a romantic twilight and half-empty. An English song about a mother who killed her child came wafting in from the recesses. It was there that I told Carmen about my childhood. She only kept repeating: 'You're hurting me, you're hurting me!' Later that night, as we were walking through Prague's New Town, people stopped and looked somewhere over our heads, as if our auras were visibly aglow. Each day via a discreet go-between I would receive a love letter from her. She called me the wolf and the master of her fate. This melancholy creature wrote her epistles in blood; even now I can smell the sweet metallic fragrance of those sheets. She occupied a small room in the Institute of Noblewomen. I would sneak in to see her after nightfall, when Prague Castle had closed down. The understanding soldiers would let me pass into the labyrinth of lanes and courtyards. The patrols of the Public Security forces, indulgent smiles on their faces, would walk around me with their dogs. Only one sergeant — who had the poetic name of Francis Birdie and a muddled heart from the environs of Assisi hidden under his uniform of a servant of evil — would always stop me, to tell me his stories full of night and tiny creatures. I would listen to him attentively, for I knew he was Carmen's medium.

"The doors to the Institute of Noblewomen are furnished with rhomboidal red glass — what arousing symbolism! Behind these doors I was greeted by a creaky staircase that led me to Carmen's door. We experienced many amorous moments behind this door. When we made love for the first time, Carmen again whispered: 'You're hurting me,' and these words came from her heart and womb. Later we made love not only there, but also in the middle of Vladislavský Hall, on the Royal Throne, on the lawn of Ledeburg Terrace, in the music pavilion, in the prison hut in Stag Moat, and in the president's villa. We made passionate, savage love, our hearts chaotic and in pain.

We hurt one another. We went for walks in the Royal Game Preserve. We would take the tram there and together experience the humid warmth of this electric abode traveling the rails through Prague. It was autumn. Once one of the castle employees gave us a lift. We were flagging taxis when his yellow Mercedes stopped for us instead. He took us to the preserve with great pomp, and then later initiated the gossip about us, for my liaison with Carmen was a secret. We went through the preserve, past the summer residence Hvězda, then walked down toward Liboce, where on each visit we would stop in the small statue-filled garden to let ourselves be enchanted by Braun's allegories, Marshal Radetzky, or the Sokol leaders with the brittle Tyrš at the head. Carmen would listen to my stories; we were grateful for the happiness we shared together. We hatched a plan to leave for the Philippines, our islands of felicity, and we searched the emblems of low-flying planes, hoping we might spot the one that would take us to Manila, where we imagined ourselves lying on the operating tables of Philippine healers, letting their quick fingers extract from our bodies our affectionate hearts and then molding them into one. In Stag Moat we played at wolf, lightly biting each other's neck. On Neruda Street we drank together new wine, burčák, the nectar of autumn; the glances of those around us elevated us to a regal state. We sought seclusion from the world in the loft of Café Arco. In our dreams we flew off to the semidarkness of a library and read clandestine scripts — we were intoxicated by this clandestine love.

"And then Neruda Street became the stage for my being abandoned. Carmen grew distant. The words: 'You're hurting me,' which I had heard a thousand times a day, rang in my ears. And she did hurt me, more than the reality of being frequently separated from one another. One day I was in the area under the Castle, sitting in the Two Suns — if you're familiar with this locale today in its pseudo-upscale garb and with its din of drunken Saxons, you may have a hard time believing the dreamy, consoling emigration I experienced there. So I was sitting over a glass of wine (in those days I primarily drank wine, which uplifted me and brought me nearer the ethereal heights where Carmen resided), and reading a book. Its author was de Nerval, and today I know who it was that guided my hand as I was browsing in the library. For that matter, during the entire time this love between Carmen and me lasted I read only two books: this one by de Nerval and toward the end Le Clézio's *Fever*. So, I was sitting over a glass of wine, trying to keep my mind on my reading, but Carmen's image was distinctly before my eyes and I was consumed by longing for her. At the time I was still able to answer this longing by going up to the Castle, despite all her pleas to the contrary, banging on her door, and fervidly making love to her. For the time being I was still living in bliss. My solitude deepened in the days that followed. I would find myself sitting more and more often in the Two Suns, despairing that it was pointless to go up to the Castle. I would go nonetheless . . . until the sympathetic guards would escort me out through the gates.

"After being separated from Carmen's body a long time I found a messenger who was willing to seek her out and bring her to me, or me to her. He has remained a stranger to me till this day. He was a chance visitor to the Two Suns who took an interest in the sadness — the same as you today — that had begun to appear on my face. I told him my story. I was unable to keep it hidden; the whole of my life was contained solely in the thought of the beloved woman. There was nothing else I could say about myself. This man said he would bring

Carmen to me. This didn't surprise me, even though I believed that besides me Carmen knew no other men in the city. So I hastily jotted down a couple of lines and let the messenger leave. I was impatient to see Carmen again. The messenger returned with a reply that ran as follows: 'Where are you, my master, where is the wolf, where has the wolfman gone, that in his place a dog has come?' Wounded by these words, I assaulted the messenger with questions. He did not answer nor divulge where Carmen lay hidden, whence the letter had come. The ensuing days were spent on the stairwell in front of Carmen's room in the Institute of Noblewomen, her letter pressed between my lips. Not until a week had passed did I go down to the area under the Castle to look for the messenger. But the man did not appear and none of the regulars at the Two Suns knew him. No one could say anything definite about him; they said he might be a stonecutter, a master who had come to repair the Samson fountain in the Royal Gardens. I impatiently waited for his unpredictable arrival, and believed him to be Samson himself, girded in lionskin and vigilant over the slumber of my dear Carmen. One evening he came. He sat down at my table so nonchalantly it was as if we had arranged the meeting. He left with another letter from me. And he returned with a joyful reply: the countess was waiting for me. He pressed her address into my trembling hand and I rushed off to her. I found her name on an apartment door on Kamenická Street. I came to the door by a drab stairwell and a hallway rank with old age and poverty. Carmen's door was ajar; she was waiting behind it. We made love in the grid of light formed by the streetlamps shining through the thin curtains. We made love without words, each devouring the other's body and prolonging the moment of bliss. It was the most beautiful of all the beautiful times Carmen and I made love. A child was conceived.

"I was then condemned to an even more profound separation. I wandered the places where we had taken walks together, laying poems for her at the spots where I sensed traces of her. I again received letters from her; they were the sole tangible bond between us during this time. They came by post, full of warm words, of ineffable love and devotion, which only accentuated our estrangement. She implored me, for the sake of our love's purity, not to look for her. She wrote me of the child growing heavy inside her body. And I desired this body. Her request for a total separation led me to the brink of madness. Not heeding her wishes, I searched for her in the Institute of Noblewomen and on Kamenická Street, until I found her — she was in a garden, standing under a shrub shedding its leaves. She was the image of a goddess, yet I had no idea it was the goddess of sorrow. I clutched her in my arms and she covered me with innumerable kisses. She clung to my body and lithely made love to me. And then, without even having completely slipped out of my embrace, she said: 'You have disobeyed my wishes and have killed your child — you have given me the strength to kill it.' After she said this I went stiff. She disentangled herself, tidied herself up, and walked off. I watched her vanish into the arbor of shrubbery, the resolution of her steps bringing me pain. She did as she said and had our child aborted in a clinic, thus we both became murderers. Since that moment I have had no news of her. She may have gone to her hometown, she may have married. Yes, she married, I know that now. At the time I only knew that she wasn't."

Lusperto fell silent and looked absently out the window. It seemed he did not notice the countryside before him, perhaps he did not even notice me, the person to whom he had confided his story. His account chilled me and made me anxious. I felt that this amorous tale, played out on so many hackneyed sets, was in fact not just another banal story of tragic love.

"But this isn't the end of it," Lusperto continued after a moment.

"The ominous language of symbols was even more acutely placed before my perception. After half a year of silence, a letter came in familiar handwriting. It was birthday greetings from Carmen. A picture drawn in her hand fell out into that July day: an aborted child, a small body lying in a turbid pool, its eyes looking at me from the black India ink. It was my first visual encounter with our child after its conception, for I count among these encounters even the pictures of children's faces Carmen and I would draw at the outset of our love. The expression on these faces was always the same; the eyes of this birthday greeting also bore this same gaze. And another recent encounter with our child once and for all put the finishing touches on my mask of sorrow. I went to visit a family who just had a child born to them. You know, it really wasn't that long ago, in fact it's on this train that I've left the people who had the child. In their child I recognized mine, the child Carmen and I had conceived. It resembled the children in the drawings. Thus in my friend's child I was able to distinguish my child, and will have to give some thought as to why it has come again into the world — why it has returned so soon to my proximity — precisely through the womb of my friend's wife. I long to return to the gardens where Carmen and I were happy together. The child has come, and it stands between us as a warning. I'm not permitted to relocate Carmen; we shall never be able to be alone in our love — this is what the child wishes to deny us. Carmen knows this, and will not allow lunacy to infect my mind. Never again will she let me near her and never again will she say: 'You're hurting me, Lusperto.' Never. And she mustn't say it, for I do hurt her, as she does me. This pain is depicted in fear."

Lusperto ended his account. He leaned back on the plush seat, closed his eyes, and became immobile. I didn't disturb him. Besides, I was getting off. At the station I was greeted by a chilly autumn breeze. In a winebar in town I sat down in an armchair, where over a grog I dispelled the thought: Carmen, were you *my* lover?

come to my house

O woman, you seek love . . .
And I?

Gérard de Nerval
Sylvie

S urely you know where the road leads, and you know the name you shall tell the driver. You are well acquainted with the homes and the landscape you shall look on from the car window. And you do know my name — so come to my house. The meadow has been readied to guide your steps to my window. I have invited you this day. I am lying on a single bed in a delirious half-sleep. Beyond the window green grass gives way to white snow. A team of wolves sweep toward the skyline. Somewhere an emerald window is aglow. Over a moat an anaemic princess inquisitively observes her face. Flowers bloom, die. Bird wings rustle. Horses sense strangers in the dark. Dogs run up to my bed, nestle close in fear. A stranger's hand grasps the handle. An ungainly giant strides the horizon. A hand involuntarily clutches a chalice. Humans like beasts in the forests. On the way to the manor a lane of poplars wave their branches as if they wished to detain the carriage. I toss about on the bed, I, a man plaited from silk by the hands of ancient crones. Count Lusperto.

Unknown voices speak from the radio. Melancholy songs from uninhabited regions. An orange sea of strangeness washes up in my ears. I do not hear your footsteps in the garden — the step of women's shoes not approaching. Where is your mouth? Where do your hands repose? What fragrance is your hair at this moment? How does your chest heave?

A large cat with nefarious eyes sits on the other side of the window, wanting to come in, to me. I run through the house confused. It is now inside, walking through the house. I take it into my arms, and it bites my hands and goes for my neck. I carry it out the door and spread apart its clamping jaws. Again it jumps through the window, toward me. It was naïve of me not to have closed it. Silence, everywhere silence. The cat bites my legs, clambers up me, sticking in with its claws. Covered in blood I run weaving between the trees, the cat biting into my shoulder.

Where is your vehicle. Come to my house. I shall share misfortune with you. On the gates: an ancient coat-of-arms in a reddening rust.

angels

A black star shines above
your head, blacker than
tempered steel in earth.

Tadeusz Nowak
The Devils

The young boy asked: "Momma, what does an angel look like, does he have feathers the color of a rainbow?"

He was holding in his fingers long, spectral feathers of a dull luster, dark pinions.

"Where'd you get those?" asked his mother with foreboding.

"They were lying in the courtyard; they fell from them as they were flying over our house — a whole host of angels flying noiselessly — neither voices, nor the tones of a harp, nor a hum could be heard. They waved their wings mechanically, like machines. The sun reflected off their matte feathers; the oily, metallic glints formed a magically beautiful kaleidoscope, even the scales of their snake bodies appeared in all colors. The saber-toothed heads of the angels were set facing one direction, due east, far beyond the horizon. In their small eyes, merely an infinite torpor."

After these words his mother shrieked and dropped the object she had been holding in her hand. She sat down at the table, trembling.

"Angels don't have black feathers," she said when she had begun to calm her breathing a little.

"Angels are white and beautiful; they don't have scaly snake bodies, nor do they have sharp teeth in narrow mouths. Angels have full lips colored by the warm blood of love, golden locks of fragrant hair. Their bodies are as delicate as the bodies of new-born babes, their feathers are finer than the feathers of a fledgling. When they fly through the heavens, they bring to mind small suns. Black feathers don't fall from them. It is said they drop downy feathers onto a house where they wish to deliver glad tidings."

"What then does a black feather mean and who does it belong to?" the boy asked pertinaciously. "If white means good news, does black mean bad news?"

The mother shook in muddled anxiety. She did not answer, she did not know what to say. The boy fiddled with the feather, observed its coloring in the window, sniffed it, and rubbed it between his fingers.

"When I smell it, it has the scent of fire. I see an image of conflagrations, parched deserts, battlefields. I see reddish images of barely perceptible distances. Images of humors spawning dread. I see tormented children, careworn women, broken men. I vividly see the twisted faces where pain has inscribed itself."

The mother, in unabated terror, searched the eyes of the boy; she saw what he was speaking about. Then silence came between them. The boy opened his mouth but his mother did not hear him; though she was screaming in nervous confusion, no sound came from her mouth. The silence was broken by the sibilant swishing of wings, a tremendous, deafening swishing. They ran out to the front of the house and bent back their heads to catch a glimpse of what was flying over their roof. The sky darkened and a gloom descended on the countryside as if a storm were approaching. But approaching was a calamity more savage, more severe: the creatures with black wings and snake bodies were in flight. The sky was teeming with them, and they were not angels, they were devils. The boy, head back looking upward, whispered a phrase similar to a magic incantation. He crumpled one of their feathers in his fingers. His eyes glistened and blurred, their gaze no longer his — as if he were leaving himself, as if his soul were departing his body through these eyes. And the next instant the boy was jumping around the yard with a maniacal look, jumping and calling upward:

"Land here, angels, land in our garden, our house is open and we're waiting for you. Your feather fell on our doorstep, we crave news, we await your message!"

The panicked mother seized the boy by his waving arms and restrained them, preventing his hands from enticing the creatures into landing in the courtyard. She had no interest in welcoming these denizens of hell into her home. She tugged at the boy in an effort to ward off the catastrophe, but he broke free of her and frenziedly continued waving and calling upward. His mother ran into the house, weeping, and, closing herself in, she waited in terror for what would happen. It was time for terror, for the devils were landing and walking around the garden, drooping their wings, shaking themselves after the long flight, stretching their legs, yawning, eyes looking around the premises, piercing glares penetrating the walls of the house, the windows, and the door, eyeing the cherry trees in the garden, chattering in an abrupt din. A thousand devils, a thousand angels from hell had descended on this garden, this courtyard, and they were preparing to enter the house.

The boy stood on the threshold of the house, words of welcome clambering up on his lips. His speech was from the depths of his heart, long concealed thoughts from the most hidden recesses of his mind. He flung himself under the legs of the hell-dwellers, a throng of whom had crowded in front of the door to the house.

"I am the bread here for your homage, I am the salt offered in your honor, I am the knife with which the sacrifice is rent, the key to the house for your noble thoughts."

The black creatures watched him with small, expressionless eyes. They grabbed him, and his body was sundered, devoured. Each portion of him passed through their entrails, that in the secluded murkiness of the orchard it could be defecated and grow into a new body.

And the boy rose from the pile of excrement, lurching drunkenly with a cheerful smile. The host of winged figures stood in a circle around him and waited for more of his words. For the meantime the house was closed and quiet.

And the boy, a phoenix arisen from feces, exclaimed:

"You shall enter the house and endow it with life; you shall breathe into its walls the vigor of your race; it awaits your instructions and it shall transform itself into a citadel."

He led the host up to the door, the lock of which he overcame with a flick of the finger, and escorted the infernal guests into the silent rooms, where in the gloom his terrified mother was waiting.

The angels laid their hands on everything in the house, the house breathed and was alive, the walls exposed their pores, bathed in sweat.

"Mother, guests are here, a little hospitality is in order!" the boy, the prince of a thousand kings, called out with slaver in the corner of his mouth. "Grant them your body, for they are tired from the journey, grant them your warmth, comfort and refresh them in your embrace!"

He pushed his mother toward the bed. She offered no resistance, mechanically retreating. He laid her under a colorful, orchid-patterned blanket.

"I have only one body, how am I to meld with so many angels?" she cried in a voice now thick with delirium.

The boy said:

"Extend yourself and the angels will be satisfied, for they are worthy of sacrifice!"

The mother, lying on the bed, pulled back the blanket, revealing her nude body: white and young. And she began to divide herself, multiply, proliferate, break apart, and grow in number until there were a thousand mothers in the house and on the premises — one for each angel to do with as he pleased. And the boy strolled among the bodies of his mother. He looked on as the angels forced their stout penises into each one and he saw these bodies scream in pain and bleed.

The revitalized house displayed a mouth on its walls and repeated over and over:

"A feather fallen from the heavens signifies news."

original eyes

You may encounter a person,
sometimes he passes you by.

Paul Linde
The Grim Reaper in Aachen

I have noticed for several weeks now that whenever I leave my building, or enter it, a detective is standing in front. They are following me, I feel them at my back, wherever I am. I feel them sitting in the same cafés, frequenting the same theaters and cinemas. I now know the faces of some of the detectives, as they have become familiar to me. One young man in a leather overcoat no longer accompanies me to all the sentimental romance films which I became fond of watching — there were twelve of them. I observed him the last few times we were there. He always followed the action of the film with concentration, his severe police countenance contrasting with the cinema's adolescent viewers. I suppose he is a psychologist; perhaps they want to know what attracts me to extravagant tales of tragic love with naïve happyendings.

Even the mail I receive now, in this time when I have grown used to a foreign presence, is of a new temper. I have been getting official summonses. I have been invited to a number of interviews at the offices of various authorities. Thus all manner of officials are inquiring into who I am, where my family comes from, where I have my château. All sorts of people are investigating the source of my income, the friends I have in this city, my lovers and casual concubines.

The mail also brings me photographs of recumbent bodies that give the impression of being in a deep sleep — only the uniformed hand that traces them with chalk reveals them as dead, reposing not on velvet but on asphalt softened by the night. Usually on the reverse side of these photos an anonymous handwriting has inscribed in black letters: "Remember, Lusperto?" And I remember nothing. Flustered by this insistence, I make a futile effort at recalling, I try to arouse the prostrate figures from the depths of my subconscious. I open the door to the past and call them by all the names I'm able to remember, but no one comes.

So I sit with my silent shadow in a café (most often in Hogo-Fogo on Salvátorská Street or in Velryba on Opatovická), and am plagued by what has been suggested to me by these anonymous letters which have accompanied the photos of the prostrate bodies. Am I the cause of their condition, am I a murderer? I dispel the notion, this intrusive thought. Thus, in a state of anxiety I wait for something to occur that will cast some light on the darkness of my doubts.

And then — while at the Royalist Club on Jilská Street — something along these lines happens. One of the guests in the club, Pavel Z., says (only to me, no one else hears our conversation):

"These are genuine, *original* eyes. We need to have eyes like these in our heads!" And while uttering these words he puts in large green eyes tinted with a little brown, as if they were agate irises. His appearance is fantastic, his face distorted by the disproportionate eyes. He looks at me for a while, wordless, and then he removes the eyes and hands them to me while saying:

"You can wear such eyes!"

I do not understand why I should be the one who can wear the genuine, original eyes; I don't feel myself to be chosen, and I don't know if I even want to be; I do not know if such a thing is desirable or even advisable; I do not know what these eyes signify. Their magnitude frightens me, as does their preternatural essence. I didn't wish for such eyes and I don't trust them. I then ask:

"What does *original* mean, where is their origin, who had such eyes? Did people have such eyes before they got the ones needed for sight, the kind of eyes we have grown accustomed to today, the kind we look with and gaze into, the kind we envisage when dreaming of young girls, the kind we are afraid of when looking into the eyes of a brute? Or are they the original eyes of celestial beings, of the angels who preceded us? Do you believe that we're the descendents of other beings, that man was given his origin by a being sent from God, an inhabitant of his heavens, a priest from his temple, a priest of the innermost sanctum, a doorman from his gates charged with the task of placing sentries at the other, less important, more distant doors? I could even believe that we are in the vestibule of the cathedral, in a place far from the altar, though inexorably on the way toward it. But I don't know, I'm not yet certain, whether we have not been designated as the sentries of this particular spot, sentries who may boast of divine favor. I sense the suspicion growing deep within me that we have arrived here only by accident, and we have no idea where we have come to, where we have settled. For I believe this: if humanity knew it was standing on the way to a temple, it would set out for it and leave this earth abandoned and the door unattended. At least the humankind I know would act like this, for there is nothing keeping it on the threshold to an unknown consecration, to an unknown divinity. Humanity is not interested in an abstract, remote god."

In my consternation I prattle on like this at great length. I hold the eyes in my hand, these great, strangely colored eyeballs, the foreign eyes which Pavel Z. alleges to be the eyes of my forebears, the eyes of my direct progenitors. As I hold them with my fingers I peer into them, searching their waning luster. Appearing before me is an image long-ago suppressed: my fingers exude the aroma of damp earth — I see the figures of stooped farmers, creatures with large eyes, cultivating the land. Tall figures with pale faces and large eyes. As if I were truly gazing into my own ancient past and recognize it, recognize thousands of years of past reality, of past scents, of sensations from trivial events that have been forgotten. I relive a long-ago, now almost unreal settlement. I experience the primal origin of humankind, the advent of the teachers, peasants, and initiators. The sensation frightens me for I feel that it is well and good that humanity has already forgotten their arrival and does not revere them as its progenitors. My awakened memory frightens me, and I would like to once again lose it. I cast aside the eyes and return them to the man who wished to give them to me as a gift. In not accepting his gift, I jettison the thought of being privileged to wear the eyes. I don't believe in their authenticity as I'm convinced they are counterfeit, a deceit and a seduction harboring a cunning intrigue within.

I leave the club. On the street I distinctly hear the footsteps of my pursuers behind me. I catch a glimpse of the contours of the detectives' figures. But what has happened is beyond recall, for all that I have experienced till now bears no resemblance to the idea I had formed of the event I was awaiting as an explanation. So I walk along the city's streets, waiting, full of foggy notions and vague feelings from what has preceded, on my way toward an uncertain future. I am distracted and vexed. Nothing I have learned this day has explained a thing to me, nothing has been clarified, I wait. I walk through the street, it's dark. I walk through a late evening, not wanting to return to my armchair, not lured back by the book lying on my table open at a favorite page, not enticed by the bottle of wine I left standing on the table before leaving the house. Not even the thought of company interests me. I no longer wish to be in the presence of the friends I was looking forward to seeing this morning, nor do I wish to look into the eyes of the girl I was thinking about this morning. I have confused desires and hazy expectations.

The street then leads me to an illuminated house; I am in a familiar place. The house is a restaurant, a hotel in which I have spent a number of important and meaningful moments. Yet it's as if I'm unable to recall a thing, as if these moments were unimportant and meaningless, as if I did not come on account of them, on account of the past, as if my steps were being guided by what was to happen next, by the fate that was in store for me.

In a movement, unthinkable even just a moment ago, I stop and wait until the nearest detective reaches me. I know about him, and I also know that he must come up to me, he cannot do otherwise. Other than me and my pursuers, no one else is here. If they would like to maintain a semblance of being inconspicuous they must continue walking toward me. And they act as I expected. After a moment the nearest detective comes abreast of me and would like to covertly pass me by. Walking on the other side, he assumes the air of a chance night stroller, slightly tottering, perhaps wanting me to think him a harmless drunk returning from a night out on the town. I cross over to his side and stop him. I don't want to ruin his act as I actually have no reason to reveal that I know who he is. I, too, am discreet. I ask for a cigarette, also slightly tottering, and I try to look like an evening drunk. Both of us well know who we are, and we both maintain appearances before the other. We hold an innocuous conversation, each of us acting as if he were someone else. Speaking like a pair of lushes, we swap experiences from the bars in which we were not, get entangled in conversation about events that never happened, talk fervidly and in torrents. We speak in detail about the evening that has unfurled itself quite differently than the way we now colorfully describe it. And we stand in front of the illuminated hotel on whose ground floor is the restaurant, open despite the late hour. While talking to one another we observe several people lounging in the room, and, continuing to follow the scenario of two boozers meeting by chance, I ask my guardian whether he wouldn't like to pop in with me for a nightcap as it would be apt to drink to our fleeting friendship, our ephemeral relationship. So we go into the restaurant and sit down at a table.

Then over drinks he, the detective, the psychologist, the doctor of friendly relations, discreetly comes to the heart of the matter, as if he were accidentally touching on the topics that interested me. He acts like a kindred soul and tries to arouse my curiosity. I take up his game since I don't want to forfeit this exceptional encounter; I feel I may be able to capitalize on it, that this meeting is decisive, never to be repeated. Thus I am willing to listen to his queries, and I respond matter-of-factly. He likely now believes that he has drawn me in, that I have no idea of his true identity, that I trust him in his role as an oddball and I'll open up to him out of an affection for eccentricity. I do open up to him, but because I want to be open.

Over drinks the test then proceeds in the form of a conversation. The detective puts innocent questions to me and I colorfully answer.

"Have you heard," he asks, "have you heard that somewhere in this city there are hidden the eyes of the fathers, an actual legend materialized. The eyes of our ancient forebears, from whose lineage we are said to have sprung. These eyes are endowed with magical power. They await their new bearer. It is said that when the right one is found, the eyes will give him an unnatural energy. I have thought for a long time that this particular legend is just one of the many mysterious tales of Prague, but it was not so long ago that I caught a glimpse of these eyes myself. Yes, I'm convinced that I saw the original eyes; they were so peculiar they couldn't have been any others. They are large green eyes that gleam like emeralds. Believe me or not, I saw them inserted into someone's sockets. Obviously they didn't manifest their hidden energy — the one who had placed them in his head was not the sought after *bearer*."

These words make me tremble. The eyes are still fresh in my memory, still burning in my palms, their incalculable power still making my fingers tingle. My companion notices my trembling, but I have made no attempt to hide it — anyway, I am aware that he knew of my meeting with Pavel Z. He was there. Yet I'm interested in finding out what else he knows about these eyes.

"What is their hidden energy, what type of energy is it that empowers the eyes' new bearer? I have only heard of them perfunctorily. In several places in the darkness of the city I sometimes encounter certain men who foist on others replicas of these eyes as souvenirs of the Prague night, but I deplore the money spent on such artless fakes. Their luster was the product of cheap kitsch."

"Yes," the detective answers, "I also know these mystery mongers of the streets. I also stop to have a look at their wares, for if you were to compare the reflection of these trinkets in toto you might be able to catch a glimpse of the original's shimmer. The one who manufactures these eyes knows it exactly." A policeman's ardor returns to his voice. As if he has forgotten about the situation that has brought us together, he becomes inflamed with the case that he is occupied with.

"The essence of these original eyes' energy is menacing. I have heard that their awaited bearer will be capable through their gaze of distinguishing who is from the line of the *initiators* of long ago, thereby bringing them together and continuing in their work. Yes, it is a terrifying essence, for if they were to be brought together they would have the power to do harm, because in the thinking of these bygone *settlers* there is no dignified place for a humankind that doesn't come from their line. This is the horror these eyes conceal. We don't want any sort of elite that would be bound together by considerations we know nothing about, by an intention with which we are unable to reckon, which we cannot begin to apprehend. We don't want some clique that is capable of saying that humanity is, in the main, aberrant and hollow. We wish to protect humanity, whatever its nature, as a matter of principle and out of responsibility for its safety."

"Isn't there some hope in the prospect that these eyes will designate you as the bearer of the original intention, of the ancient blood, and guide you to your task?" I inquire, and he shrieks:

"No, no . . . this is to be feared . . . if one were to be designated the bearer he would become a machine, an instrument of an unforeseen purpose. He would cease being himself and become a component of society, lose his identity."

The fear he expresses is sincere, but I feel I cannot share with him the fear I experienced as I was holding the eyes in my hand. It was of a different nature, it emanated from a different sensation — losing my identity was not what frightened me. I was afraid of committing murder; I had a palpable fear of feeling unrestrained, a sensation which absolves one of everything — it was the feeling of superiority that so frightened me. I turn to my companion with a new query:

"Is it true that the police are searching for these eyes?"

Vacillating, he does not answer at once.

"I suppose . . . they could be searching for them. After all, it would be the logical thing to do as these eyes do pose a threat."

I continue:

"I have heard that in connection with the eyes the police have been keeping under surveillance a certain count, an eccentric of sorts, likely a stranger."

He is taken aback by my question, and he runs through in his mind whether I know who he is. I mull over whether the police knew about the original eyes before I did; whether they were also tailing Pavel Z., and anticipated our meeting in the club; whether the photographs of corpses that I have been receiving are directly connected with the sensation of a sovereign right to determine the life and death of people, which stole into my mind as I was holding the eyes in the palm of my hand; whether a distortion of habitual, conventional thought has led me to suspect that these eyes, which even this official has called authentic and original, are spurious and false, or was my alarm correct and well-founded. I am becoming increasingly convinced that my sense of the eyes' spuriousness is correct. I sense a noose tightening around my neck as well, and I know that I'm pulling it ever tighter by my inner uncertainty.

The detective looks at me with eyes also uncertain, and then he says diffidently and in an unpolice-like manner:

"There is a mysterious count in town whom we know very little about. There are the eyes, there are other mysterious people who frequent the same places as the count, there are murders in the middle of the night. We live in jeopardy. We ask the shadows for the cause of these attacks. Slinking along the ground on all fours, we search the shades, that they might lead us to the murderer."

"And who are you, what sort of role do you play in this performance of the Theater of Fear?" I now ask directly. I'm curious about the answer, the gist of which I already know. The man now takes up the game wholly, clearly more deeply involved than he originally wished:

"I am one of those who fear, this is my role," he answers.

"I am a reader of ancient tomes, an habitué of romantic films, a photographer of corpses, a devotee of expected happyendings, a civil servant behind a partition, a reader of completed questionnaires, a decipherer of reports and tax returns, a critic of replies, a seeker of treasures, a charmer of snakes. I breakfast in buffets, lunch in expensive restaurants, and dine in brothels. I am the shade of a shadowy body, a spider in a foreign web, a hunter in a foreign hunting ground, a servant of servants." He speaks wearily and openly, looking at me with opaque blue eyes.

"And who are you?" he then adds.

"I am a former author of books, a writer of folk phrases, an originator of love stories, a director of romantic films with the expected ending, a man in front of office partitions, a completer of questionnaires, reports, and tax returns, a man responding to questions, an accumulator of treasures, a burier of chests, a hand stroking a snake.

I breakfast in brothels, lunch in expensive restaurants, and dine in buffets. I am a body without a shadow, a spider without a web, the owner of a hunting ground where there is no hunting, a master without a servant." I talk long and dangerously with a desire to confess, to let my name resound in such a way that it will take flight, beating its wings under the ceiling of this incidental bar. I do not utter my name, however, because my table companion says:

"I saw the eyes we're talking about in your hands. You returned them, you didn't put them into your head and you didn't look through them, you didn't gaze at the world through their sight." As if afraid of my reaction he grasps the butt of his weapon under the table. He grips his revolver, resolving to use it on me if I do something unexpected. I smile at him with these words:

"I saw the eyes in my hand and I was afraid they were frauds, that the jewel had no value." These words placate him, and he lets go of his gun.

"I noticed you were frightened," he says further and then falls silent.

"I was frightened. I was afraid the eyes belonged in my head, that I was perceiving the straggling figures of the *peasant farmers* who sowed noble seed among the weeds of humanity; I was afraid they would give me the power to perform acts I had no wish to perform; I was afraid it would be possible to perceive such things through them; I was afraid these eyes were truly, genuinely original; I was afraid that in their *verity* lies their *falsity* — I am Herbert Lusperto de Pedurac."

The man looks wearily at the bottom of his glass, and with a mechanical motion he produces his revolver and lays it on the table:

"I know who you are."

And I, too, lay on the table my weapon: a pistol inlaid with silver displaying the visage of a ruby-eyed snake on its haft. He regards it intently, with a question in his eyes.

"I am Detective Zamora," he says. He is now holding his gun in his hand. I quickly grab mine.

"I know who you are," I also say. We take aim at one another over the tranquil table on which the glasses of alcohol are standing. It is quiet. The other guests in the place are engrossed in their own thoughts; the waiter stands by the bar, a blank expression on his face. Outside in the dark street a car occasionally drives by, its sound melancholy. Time passes.

From a roof window someone's hand lets fly a bat with an encoded message in its membraneous ear.

pilgrimage

Slowly they walked next to one another,
holding hands like children.

Paul Leppin
Daniel Jesus

A strange morning, perhaps night still. Earth, damply redolent, clings to our feet, restraining them — into it they sink. We're descending a slope, our gait very much like sliding. There is nothing funny about this, it is difficult. We are no longer children and this is not a game. We're descending into a valley where we suspect there'll be a village at the bottom as from time to time we catch sight of some houses, a wooden shack, the vague contours of roofs. We're descending the slope and we are not exactly sure why we are forcing our way through an undergrowth whose scent is so perfidious and heady that any feeling of anxiety is forgotten. We are anxious, and properly so. It is not clear what has driven us out into this black morning, what has compelled us to let sharp twigs scratch our faces and hands, what has made us set out on this journey, the meaning of which eludes us.

A prime mover certainly exists, one must exist, for we would not have willingly abandoned our heated homes to set out on such a dubious adventure. We're descending and nearing the bottom, not symbolically, but in fact, for the outlines of wooden houses are coming into focus. Their darkness is palpable: no light anywhere that could provide at least a hint of human presence. Our steps, the sounds of our steps, are out of place in these surroundings — they do not belong here. More fitting would be to approach this place in the rigidity of a levitating monk, instead of like this, as a group of puny, apprehensive people.

As we draw near, the slope changes into flatland, and we now walk through a soft meadow. The marshland village emits no sound — quiet — no rooster keeping watch for the coming dawn, no dog keeping an eye on the safety of the dwellings, no cat inquisitively looking at us from the roofs, no cattle shifting in a warm stable. Nothing. Nothing is here. And yet our objective is here. It was precisely here we set out for; it is here we are seeking an answer; to here we have made our way, that we may find an answer. We are seeking an answer and no one has uttered a question. Our journey is without beginning, but its objective is steadfast, immoveable. It is before us and we await its message.

Between the houses there is an eddy of wind, which disturbs the image of silence. The silence has danced diffusely, unfolded in its motion, vigorous and gaining in strength, oppressive — a vigorous, whirling silence. A sensation overcomes us like that a pilgrim often may have before the gates of a sacred site. We are where we have longed to be, at journey's end. The place is completion, reality. We sense an answer, a sense resolute and decisive. We know the answer, we know that it has been uttered. The exact wording is immaterial.

We are in the middle of a black village and converse in whispers, for an event is approaching, the denouement. We come to a door, the only door here that is open, exhorting us. We enter, going in, coming on a visit to this house. Having wandered for a long time, we yearn for a friendly clasp of the hand, for the intimate softness of an armchair, for a cup of coffee that will warm our hands in a moment of carefree relaxation.

In the middle of the house is a comfortable armchair, an armchair from the dreams of weary wayfarers. But rather than empty it is filled and uninviting, sunken in a pained shape under the heavy body of the man who occupies it, the master of the house. The man sits in the armchair in battledress. An Adonis with a visage now old, a corpulent god girded by a strap of leather. Menacing in his silence. His eyes are open but his gaze is absent, fixed somewhere far beyond us. As he mechanically rocks in his chair he doesn't speak, doesn't welcome us. Is he the objective? Is he a prophet or a priest? We approach this serene man of divine essence. We shake his shoulders through the ornate epaulettes. With our hands we draw pictures before his eyes, indicating our presence. It is pointless, we suspect that it is pointless. His countenance gives the impression of knowing everything about us, not only so negligible a fact as that we are standing in his proximity, by the armchair in his house. His greatness eclipses our diminutiveness. With a patronizing expression he suddenly assimilates himself to our laity, drops down to our lowness, and begins to speak in our language:

"You have come to me, to take a seat at my table." It is not a question, it is a statement, for we all know that we desire nothing else.

"You have come beset with vague questions to a place that is an answer, I am here as an answer and I answer. What is it you wish to ask, what do people usually ask when they have undertaken a laborious journey for an answer? You ask where is the prime mover of existence; where does God reside, where is His golden throne, and whether He even exists; what grants you your existence and the strength for it; for what purpose do you surmount obstacles and raise yourself after falling; what are you pursuing and what informs your steps? I am an answer for I am also one who asks. Your journey has led you here, to this place, in a village which is silent and deserted — as inert as a question — to the house which contains my armchair and my inertia. I answer because I myself ask — I give voice to that which you didn't want to formulate. I sit here and ponder, and I ask: Where is God; where has He gone; why is the armchair that I have provided Him in my room vacant; why has He not tasted the food I have laid at His place at my table; why is the water in the glass for Him turning fetid; why doesn't He read my books; why doesn't He come when I pull the bellrope so that He will hear me?" Thus he speaks and we understand him. We cry out:

"Where is He, why have we come here if He isn't here? Why are we in this place if God isn't here? Why are we in this house where an old man in military uniform sits in a chair and waits for Him to come? Why aren't we also sitting in our chairs and waiting for Him there? After all, we have provided armchairs, have prepared food and water. We, too, have sounded the bells so He would hear us. Would He rather come here than to us? We looked for Him in the temples, chapels, and cathedrals, and He wasn't there. We searched for Him in the monasteries and hermitages, and He hadn't come. We waited by the crucifixes at the crossroads, and He didn't go there. Why have we come here?"

The soldier smiled:

"I have been on battlefields, I have passed through prisons, camps, famines and I felt Him, He was close. He, too, went the same way. I knew of Him by the beds of the dying, in the hospitals and in the cemeteries. He went before me. I saw His vestiges though I never caught sight of Him. I sit here, waiting for Him. I know his vestiges, thus I recognize His substance."

"You know His vestiges and recognize His substance?" we cried tumultuously.

"On what basis have you recognized it, how is it possible to recognize it? What do His vestiges look like, that from them you have already inferred a substance?!"

the guest

Stars rise upward
afraid of falling.

Paul Linde
The Grim Reaper in Aachen

He flew in amid a warm summer night when the stars, planets, and low-flying satellites could be clearly seen, when the Milky Way was transparently white and appeared to be a path along which cosmic pilgrims travel to Earth. He came in a fantastically shaped starship, attended by a luminous tail, a kaleidoscope of coruscating colors, of unknown hues. He landed in the middle of golden fields, alighted to the aroma of wheat — an elegant young man in a fastidiously selected black suit, pale Selenius, a meloncholy visitor here. He left his ship, and with a smile and nimble gait he set off down the road to the village. As he walked he was moved by the beauty of the countryside. He kept walking and came upon homes, human dwellings, the places where people slept, respiring bodies, idle figures, beings exhausted with travail and daily bustle. He was approaching the village. This mysterious stranger — unexpected, let alone awaited — was now drawing near.

The night was black and warm, the day's heat having left its traces. The fields were calm, purling like the surface of a lake, their gold shining in the darkness like the luster of the stars high above them. Among the first houses he came to a dog awoke; half-asleep and true to his function as sentry he began to bark. Selenius pet him with a glance and also tried to bark. This first being he had encountered here was dear to Selenius. He stood behind the fence and growled at the dog, at this mongrel from the silent village. The dog became unsettled, having been startled by the unusual behavior of the passer-by, and ran off to the back of the house. Selenius continued on to the village, the whole of which had already come to life with the sounds of dogs. Here and there a light flickered in a window and a human outline looked out searchingly. Prying faces appeared behind the windows, mistrustful faces peering into the night. Selenius smiled at these friendly windows, once he even waved his graceful fingers. And the dogs calmed down, as there was no one posing a threat.

Selenius sat on the village square and waited for dawn. Then he rose from his spot in the anticipation that the people he had seen in the windows would come out of their homes. He was waiting for them, for he had noticed that he and they were similar. He watched with delight as the first came out and crossed the village square. He watched the men going to work and compared their anatomy with his own. They were very similar, the difference was in their certain shapelessness — they were more paunchy, more flaccid, yellow and red — and their faces, as well as the expressions they wore, were somehow lacking symmetry. As they walked around him, they looked at him curiously, though evasively, as if they were not even able to keep their eyes on him or endure his gaze. Wanting to speak with them, he greeted them. But his salutation was not returned and the attempt at conversation came to nothing.

Selenius waited for others to come out. After some time the village came back to life, but lazily, languidly, not in the way he had imagined a village so beautiful would live. And what's more, the light of day exposed many details that night in its mercy had concealed. The village, then, lost its charm, for what had created harmony at night now displayed a battered face, spiritual poverty. As if the entire place bore something of the asymmetry of its inhabitants. He felt out of place here. He was out of place here, yet he had not expected the awareness of being foreign would be so strong. He saw that these people were similar to him, but the similarity of their hearts with that of Selenius's was no doubt at an even greater variance than any differences in anatomy. He did not understand the willful silence, the mistrust reflected in their glances, a mistrust verging on irrational hatred. He greeted all those walking past and tried to speak with them. True, a few did return the greeting, but cooly, restrained as if in shock, uncertain as if they were doing something illicit, uncommon, even forbidden.

Selenius walked around the square for a while and tried to strike up conversations with the people. His efforts were in vain. He did catch several hidden smiles, but all the same, those who had sent them eventually averted their eyes.

So it went the whole day until evening again began to draw near. Then the women stepped out from the houses. They were creatures more beautiful, and for Selenius, more acceptable than the men he had seen during the day. He addressed them and they stopped, answered him, and giggled. This astounded Selenius — finally some of the creatures were conversing with him, finally he had discovered that someone understood him, that someone had a sense of what he was actually saying. The women laughed, hung on his body, stroked his cheeks.

They took his hand and led him to one of the houses, to a tavern, which Selenius had not the slightest sense of. There they sat him down at a table and ordered him drinks: liquors, wines, and colored sodas.

They clinked glasses with him, laughing the whole time.

Then the men entered the room. They finally came nearer to him and even touched him. They raised him off the chair, dragged him out into the hall, pummeled him with their fists, and kicked him when he fell to the ground.

"He shows up here like some seducer, wanting to be more attractive than the men of this town, and our women take to flirting with him; we have to beat him, hurt him, destroy him!" was the first sentence he had heard from them. And the last, because he died.

It was night. The stars were smiling above the golden fields. Dead Selenius lay in the hall by the bathroom of a country tavern. All the suns in the universe in one instant rose and set.

the social season in town m.

A hand clenched the amulet,
a mouth touched the goblet.
Quivering quiet.

Paul Linde
The Grim Reaper in Aachen

As the sun drew close to the earth and the danger loomed that the world would end, Lusperto de Pedurac was standing in Town M., holding the hand of Anna Sachs. It was evening in Town M. They were standing in the shadow of a church, whose steps were liquid — that is, they appeared to be liquid, as if flowing from the gatehouse, decrepit with age, broken, treaded down and worn smooth. Lusperto was lost in reverie and his palm was sweating; he feared the girl whose hand he was clutching.

"It is evening, and it is our nature to enjoy ourselves in company," he implored, and urged Anna to step away from the church. On the gates of the edifice glimmered a notice inscribed by a crude hand:

DUE TO THE ILLNESS OF THE BONES IN THE OSSUARY
THE TABERNACLE IS CLOSED

"Come rejoice with the living, the dead will grant us only their pestilence," he added, and they walked through a town constructed of low houses. Their journey further was swift and without words. They ended in a palace garden already darkened by night.

"Our love is forbidden in its sacredness," said Lusperto. He embraced Anna Sachs, pressed against her, kissed her and caressed her; his hand found her breast, the nipples pointed in expectation; his hand found the fine down of her sex. He kissed her lips, her breasts, her belly. And he was overcome by melancholy. Town M. was now dark, and fever crept into the lovers' bodies.

"O pure one, you are distressed and your eyes are closing," Lusperto then said, and he led Anna Sachs to a bench in a recess of the garden.

"The stars are watching us, waiting, their eyes half-closed."

He sat Anna down and unbuttoned her blouse, caressed her breasts and breathed in their fragrance.

"Company is awaiting our arrival, let us hurry." He unfastened her skirt and undressed her. Anna Sachs was nude, nude and beautiful. They made love in the darkness of the park — Lusperto, in the darkness, whispered:

"I am inside you, I feel your soul, I am inside you, I feel the quivering of your viscera."

Fever entered the lovers' bodies, their limbs entwined and fervid.

"This pain, this awful pain, it's magnificent," said Anna Sachs, and her mouth sought out a stigma on Lusperto's chest.

Later into the night, they then opened a door and entered a spacious room. The hall was noisy and bright; a wild, onerous music was playing there. The dancing couples only perceived one another, here there were no distant gazes. So the lovers stepped over the threshold and entered — an official event. Without giving them so much as a single glance, those present saw that the awaited couple had come in. A ceremonial welcome. Lusperto and Anna Sachs mingled among the dancers. Their bodies formed a whole: the rhythm of the dance, the rhythm of their love-making.

"If I look at your hands," said Anna, "the inside of my body is burned, for with them you have touched my innermost; if I look into your eyes, the core of my mind is sered, for with them you have touched my thoughts; if I look at your lips, my throat is scorched, for with them you have touched my tongue; if I look at your sex, I am consumed completely, for with it you have touched everything." Lusperto let out a cry and looked down at the floor. The dance's rhythm accelerated and the legs of both barely kept up with the new tempo.

With a heavy tongue Lusperto then said: "The bed we have arisen from has already turned to dust."

The music broke off and the couples were embraced by silence. The lights flashed, giving the signal. The people sat down at the tables and ordered drinks from the waiters. Lusperto crossed the hall with Anna. They stopped at the serving counter. Town M. was silent, inquisitive. They ordered drinks and Town M. smiled.

"How can we leave this place if it is required that we remain?" asked Anna with a compassionate smile.

"How can we patiently wait for the arrival of the wizard if we do not feel like waiting but know that we must?"

"There is no need to wait, the wizard is present," answered Lusperto. He took hold of Anna Sachs's hand, "the wizard is present and I am holding his hand." And he held the wizard by the hand, gazing into the visage of a child-ancient, a woman-beast.

The thunderclap was attended by a white light. The thunderclap carried them away. It was noon — they were sitting in a castle yard, their eyes luminous. The hostess inquired:

"Have you come in goodwill or ill?" and added: "Take my question as a courtesy, it is necessary for the choice of drinks I shall prepare for you."

"In good," answered Lusperto, "In good, with pure intent — we have stepped out of our cellar and we want to hear the language of space."

"The language of space is a festive fanfare designated for your shade," said the hostess. "Live a moment in my radiance."

They lived in her radiance and listened to the language of light. It was a time of news proclaimed far and wide, an age of dialed telephone numbers, a time of radio broadcasts and mediated voices.

"My servants cheat me," said the hostess, the lady of the castle, and she grew morose.

"My servants murder and steal." At that moment one of the murderers bent over Lusperto and poured him a glass of dark wine.

"My servants murder and write of their exploits in magazines!" shrieked the hostess and she spat. She spat and her movement attracted five small dachsunds. She stroked and fondled them.

"Town M. is in the midst of the social season; Town M. awaits an event; Town M. lays flowers at the feet of Herbert Lusperto de Pedurac and Anna Sachs."

In the small hours of morning, with heads full of wine, Lusperto and Anna left for home, to a museum of peculiar shadows in whose attic was a made bed where sleep was awaiting them. They lay down and the shadows of the attic materialized as felines. The soft flitting about reverberated off the rafters. The lovers lay next to one another, looking upward — around their bed stood the shadows of the cats.

"I fear your touch," said Anna, "I am pregnant, I am married, I am not yours."

"I am afraid to touch your flesh," said Lusperto, "you are pregnant, you are married, you are not mine." With apprehension, he uncovered the quilt covering Anna's body, a white body, the scent of a pregnant belly. He embraced this body, pressed himself to it, and entered it. The mouth of Anna's sex received him. They made love gently and in silence. In the morning Anna said:

"I had no pain, our bodies belonged to one another . . . !"

And they went out to the street where the light was already quite bright — inexorable, denuding. Anna walked up the street and Lusperto watched her from behind, waiting for her to turn around, waiting for a gesture. She did not turn and Lusperto went down the street, also not looking back. So it had to be, — their love was genuine. They belonged to one another in the same way that opposite ends of the road belong to one another. Absolutely — irrevocably.

About the Author

MAFA, Jiří Turek

Ewald Murrer was born in 1964 in Prague. In the 1980s he was employed by the Office of the President as a gardener at Prague Castle. After the revolution in 1989 he dedicated himself solely to literature and was for three years the editor of the influential journal for young poets *Inicialý*, then poetry editor of the prestigious Mladá Fronta publishing house. His first "officially" published volume of poetry appeared in 1992. Since then he has published five further volumes of poetry and prose. In addition, his work has appeared in anthologies and journals internationally, including *Child of Europe* (Penguin), *Daylight in Nightclub Inferno* (Catbird) and *This Side of Reality* (Serpent's Tail). With the publication of *The Diary of Mr. Pinke* (Twisted Spoon, 1995), Murrer's first volume to appear in English translation, he began to receive international attention as one of the most promising poets of his generation. Murrer currently is editor-in-chief of the weekly Mladá Fronta Dnes magazine.

Dreams at the End of the Night by Ewald Murrer •
originally published as *Sny na konci noci* (Brno: Petrov,
1996) • translated by Howard Sidenberg • drawings by
Richard Teschner • text set in Janson • design by Chaim •
first edition published in 1999 by Twisted Spoon Press,
P.O. Box 21—Preslova 12, 150 21 Prague 5, Czech Rep.,
www.terminal.cz/~twispoon • printed in the Czech Republic
by Tiskárny Havlíčkův Brod • previous versions in slightly
different form appeared as follows: "Temptation," *The
Prague Revue*, 2, (1996); "End of the Circle," *Heat*, 7,
(1998) • the translator gratefully thanks Kevin Blahut and
Michaela Hájková for their invaluable comments on the
manuscript.

Twisted Spoon books are distributed by:
SUBTERRANEAN CO., P.O. Box 160, 265 South Fifth Street,
Monroe, OR 97456, subco@clipper.net • SMALL PRESS DIS-
TRIBUTION, 1341 Seventh St., Berkeley, CA 94710,
spd@spdbooks.org • MARGINAL DISTRIBUTION, 277 George
Street N., Unit 103, Peterborough, Ontario, CAN K9J
3G9, marginal@ptbo.igs.net.